DAWN OVER ZERO

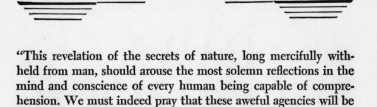

"This revelation of the secrets of nature, long mercifully withheld from man, should arouse the most solemn reflections in the mind and conscience of every human being capable of comprehension. We must indeed pray that these aweful agencies will be made to conduce to peace among the nations, and that instead of wreaking measureless havoc upon the entire globe, they may become a perennial fountain of world prosperity."

From a statement by Winston Churchill
announcing the atomic bomb

DAWN
OVER ZERO

THE STORY OF THE
ATOMIC BOMB

William L. Laurence

SECOND EDITION, ENLARGED

19 53

Alfred A. Knopf   New York

This is a Borzoi Book, published by Alfred A. Knopf, Inc.

Published August 22, 1946
Second Edition, Enlarged, October 1947
Reprinted, July 1950
Reprinted, April 1953

TO
FLORENCE

INTRODUCTION

EARLY in 1939 I attended a meeting of the American Physical Society at Columbia University, at which a group of leading physicists were discussing a revolutionary discovery—uranium fission. I watched them write strange hieroglyphics on the blackboard, heard them speculate about the possibilities of a chain reaction, about fantastic amounts of energy being liberated. And as I sat there listening and watching, the figures on the blackboard suddenly started a chain reaction in my brain.

When the meeting was over, I rushed up to Enrico Fermi and Niels Bohr. "Does all this add up to an atomic bomb?" I blurted out.

The two Nobel prize winners looked startled. Bohr looked up at the ceiling. Fermi eyed me quizzically.

"Theoretically that may be possible, some day," said Fermi when the silence was finally broken. "But not for a long time," he added, as an afterthought.

"How long?" I persisted.

"Maybe twenty-five, maybe fifty years."

"Maybe Hitler will make one in much less time," I shot back.

Thus began my version of "the Big Egg and I."

I went home that night very much perturbed. War at that time had become a certainty. It was equally certain to me that this was a chance the Nazis were not likely to pass up. Knowing the state of our unpreparedness and the tremendous effort it would take to put uranium fission to work in a military weapon, it seemed to me almost a foregone conclusion that the Nazis would get there first. I was a frightened man.

I did not know that there were other frightened men like me, particularly among the exiled scientists, who knew what time of day it was. Only six years later did I learn that, shortly after my conversation with him, Dr. Fermi had gone to Washington to interest our armed services in the possibilities of an atomic weapon, and that, as might have been expected, he had been given the good old-fashioned run-around. Neither did I learn until much later that from the very beginning scientists had agreed among themselves not to discuss military applications openly. The world for me soon became one vast Poesque pit over which a uranium pendulum was slowly swinging down, with the difference that in this case the victim was not aware of his danger.

While I had written a number of articles for the *New York Times* on uranium fission during 1939, I had purposely refrained from mentioning its devastating possibilities as a military weapon. Then, bit by bit, through my questioning of exiled scientists, I learned that my fears had been only too well founded. The Nazis, it came out, had set aside a special institute in Berlin to which they had assigned two hundred of their top scientists to develop an atomic bomb and an atomic fuel.

During the period of the "sitzkrieg," when the world was daydreaming about a "phony war," I was having nightmares about Nazi scientists putting the finishing touches on an atomic bomb. That was the only explanation for the Hitlerite hordes' sitting in idleness that seemed to make sense. They were waiting, I reasoned, for something big, something with which to overwhelm the world. Then, in March 1940, came the announcement that the first bits of uranium 235 had been isolated and had proved the correctness of what until then had been based largely on hypothesis. That clinched the argument. If American scientists could concentrate U.235 with the pitifully meager resources at their disposal, then it was practically certain that the Nazi scientists, with all the industrial and other resources of Germany at their disposal, could separate amounts great enough to be used in a military weapon.

I realized that the time had come when the American people, and the democratic world, should be made aware of the danger. I had been planning the story for a later date when my wife intervened. Why wait? If the world is to come to an end, let it know the worst as soon as possible. Her insistence, as it turned out, saved the day, for in less than a week the blitzkrieg against France was on in full fury, and I would never have been given the amount of space necessary to tell the story in full, nor the prominent front-page display it received.

So, after taking the precaution to assure my managing editor that I was not attempting to emulate Jules Verne and H. G. Wells as writers of scientific fiction, I prepared a seven-column story for the *Times* in which I told the world of the isolation for the first time of minute bits of uranium 235, pointing out that one pound of it would be the equivalent in energy to 5,000,000 pounds of coal or 15,000 tons of TNT. I reported what the Nazis were doing about it and what it would mean if they were to get ahead of us. The story appeared on page one, Sunday, May 5, 1940. I had hoped that the facts would galvanize Washington into action. But all the article did, so far as I could see at the time, was to arouse Senator Sheridan Downey of California, who inserted it in the *Congressional Record* as part of a long speech on the threat of atomic energy to the petroleum industry of his state.

My next step was to write an extensive article for the *Saturday Evening Post,* the editors of which finally accepted it for publication after a certain amount of understandable skepticism. It appeared in the issue of September 7, 1940, under the title "The Atom Gives Up." In August 1945, after President Truman had announced the dropping of the first atomic bomb on Hiroshima, the *Post* reprinted several hundred thousand copies of the article with the blurb that it "had told the story behind the atomic bomb a full five years ahead." Later the *Post* revealed that it had been requested by the FBI to take the issue of September 7, 1940 out of circulation and that similar requests had been made of libraries throughout the country. Furthermore, all those asking for that particular issue were investigated.

After VE day I was ushered into a very private office of the Manhattan District and shown a number of documents captured from the Nazis. Among them, beautifully preserved in cellophane, were my articles in the *Times* and the *Post*.

In addition to articles, I also kept bombarding some of the top-notch physicists with letters urging them to get busy.

After Pearl Harbor I tried my damnedest to get into some form of active war service and realized for the first time, like others of my age group, that, as far as the armed forces were concerned, I was just an old man. I welcomed the opportunity when I was asked to serve as a consultant to the Medical Division of the National Research Council and to the Office of the Army Surgeon General.

But the specter of the atomic bomb never left me, and as the war progressed and the Nazis kept issuing their frequent threats of new devastating secret weapons, I was sure that we could expect them to spring an atom-bomb attack almost any day. By that time editors had been asked by the Office of Censorship to refrain from writing about atomic fission or anything relating to the subject. This regulation, I learned, applied also to the speculation about a possible atomic bomb being the Nazi secret weapon, as each article I prepared on the subject was returned by the censor with a plea not to publish, despite the fact that the information related only to enemy secrets.

Then one day, early in April 1945, my managing editor and friend, Edwin L. James, called me into his office.

"A General Groves is coming from Washington to see you," he informed me.

"Who is he, and what do you suppose he is after?"

"Don't know. Maybe they are after you to find out how you know so much about Nazi secret weapons!"

By that time, through a process of piecing together stray bits of information gathered from various sources, I knew in a general way that we had atomic plants in Oak Ridge, Tennessee, and also somewhere in the states of Washington and New Mexico. While I had never heard of General Groves, the possibility of his connection with these plants immediately suggested itself. "I think I know what he is after," I said.

On the day General Groves arrived, he first had a private conversation with Mr. James. An interminable time seemed to pass before I was finally called in. Then things began moving rather fast.

"We want you to come to work for us," said General Groves.

"I have been waiting for a long time for an opportunity to serve. When do I start?"

"As soon as possible. We will tell you all about it when you come to Washington."

"I hope I'll be permitted to go to Tennessee, Washington, and New Mexico," I said with an air of one who knew what it was all about, though not even a hint had been dropped as to what my job was to be.

"You'll go farther than that," said Mr. James.

Thus began my journey through Atomland-on-Mars,

which reached its climax at one minute past noon on August 9, 1945, several miles in the air above Nagasaki, when I watched the second, and last, atomic bomb used in warfare explode in a pillar of fire that reached 60,000 feet into the stratosphere and brought the greatest war in history to a victorious end.

By July 12, 1945 I had been with the Atomic Bomb Project (Manhattan District) a little over two months, Atomic Time, the equivalent of a lifetime or more in non-atomic calendar time. I had flown more than 35,000 miles and had visited all the secret plants, which at that time no one mentioned by name—Oak Ridge, Hanford, Los Alamos; the Martian laboratories at Columbia, Chicago, and California universities. I had seen things no human eye had ever seen before, things that no one had ever thought possible. I had watched men work with heaps of uranium 235 and plutonium great enough to blow any city off the map. I had prepared scores of reports on what I had seen, every one of them marked "Top Secret" and locked in a special top-secret safe.

Shortly after I joined the project General Groves asked me to prepare a list of subjects I intended to write about. Item No. 26 on the list read: "Eyewitness account of test in New Mexico," to which I added in parentheses: "provided eyewitness survives." Another item read: "Eyewitness account of mission over Japan," again with the proviso of the eyewitness's survival. On the afternoon of July 15 in New Mexico, when I protested to General Groves that the observation post assigned to me was too far away ("How do you expect me to give an eyewitness account twenty miles from the scene?") he reminded me that he had a certain interest in having the eyewitness survive.

"You'll see all you need to see," he assured me as he rode off to attend to more important business. As it turned out, my observation spot on a hill was much more advantageous than his, since he had to lie in a deep trench, "face down, head away from zero," for the first seconds of the flash, whereas I could stand up and face the spectacle.

That the "survival of the eyewitness" could by no means be taken for granted, even at a distance of twenty miles, became evident to me from the nature of some advance material I was asked to prepare. One piece was a purely fictitious account to be used in the event of an unforeseen catastrophe following the first atomic explosion in the New Mexico desert, resulting in great damage over a wide area, including the sudden total disappearance without trace of a large number of the country's outstanding scientists, not to mention a certain member of the journalistic fraternity. The secret was to be kept at all costs, and so a plausible tale had to be ready for immediate release, minus by-line, of course, since by the time of publication the "eyewitness" also would most likely have been a highly turbulent radioactive ghost.

One of my last acts before leaving for Alamogordo was to write a letter to Mr. James, the only one I sent to the outside world, excepting, of course, letters to my wife. It read in part as follows:

"Forgive me for not writing sooner. I have been busier than the proverbial one-armed paper-hanger ever since I left. I have covered lots of ground and seen things that made me dizzy. In fact, I have been in a constant state of bewilderment now for some two months and the biggest surprises are still ahead.

"The story is much bigger than I could imagine, fantastic, bizarre, fascinating and terrifying. When it breaks it will be an Eighth Day wonder, a sort of Second Coming of Christ yarn. It will be one of the big stories of our generation and it will run for some time. It will need about twenty columns on the day it breaks. This may sound overenthusiastic, but I am willing to wager you right now that when the time comes you will agree that my estimate is on the conservative side.

"This is not just one big story. There are at least twenty-five individual page-one stories to be given out following the break of the big news. When it does break, you will undoubtedly think of many other angles, national, international, political, diplomatic, industrial, and what not.

"The world will not be the same after the day of the big event. A new era in our civilization will have started, with enormous implications for the postwar period, both from a military and from an industrial standpoint.

"At present I am one of the few men in the world who know the complete story, with the exception of dates. The security regulations are so stringent that I am afraid even to talk to myself. Even my identity is kept a deep secret and I find myself slinking around corners for fear someone may recognize me.

"While the job is naturally exhilarating and thrilling, it has been a tremendous weight on one's shoulders. It goes against one's grain to write a big story and mark it 'Top Secret' and lock it up in a safe. I am looking forward to the day when I can dig up a good story and dash to the nearest Western Union office."

In the summer of 1946 I watched the explosions of the fourth and fifth atomic bombs at Bikini, which, with the explosions over New Mexico and Nagasaki, bring the total I have seen up to four. I also saw the bomb that demolished Hiroshima, though I did not accompany the mission because of my late arrival at Tinian, in the Marianas, because of a mishap to my plane on my way to Honolulu. Only three other men have seen as many of the bombs in action as I have, and no one has seen more. No other civilian has seen as many.

This book is the story of as much of it as can be told now and for some time to come.

ACKNOWLEDGMENTS

TO Major General Leslie R. Groves, who afforded me the opportunity of many lifetimes, I offer high esteem and deep gratitude.

For their generous assistance and many personal kindnesses, my profound thanks go to the following:

Major General Thomas F. Farrell
Colonel Kenneth D. Nichols
Colonel Stafford L. Warren
Colonel F. T. Matthias
Lieutenant Colonel W. A. Consodine
Captain Bradley G. Seitz
Lieutenant G. O. Robinson
Lieutenant Milton R. Cydell
Mr. Roy Hageman

Among the scientific group I wish to express my profound gratitude for their generous help to:

Dr. Ernest O. Lawrence
Dr. Arthur H. Compton
Dr. J. R. Oppenheimer
Dr. Luiz W. Alvarez
Dr. Richard P. Feynman
Dr. James R. Coe, Jr.
Dr. H. T. Wensel.

I want to take this opportunity to express my appreciation to Mr. Arthur Hays Sulzberger, president and publisher, and Mr. Edwin L. James, managing editor, of the *New York Times,*

ACKNOWLEDGMENTS

for their many kindnesses, including permission to reprint some of the material in this book.

To my wife, Florence, a good soldier in the army of "atomic-bomb widows," to whom this book is dedicated, my profound gratitude for her invaluable assistance in its preparation.

W. L. L.

CONTENTS

ILLUSTRATIONS

(Follow page 289)

ILLUSTRATIONS

(ALL PHOTOS OF THE TESTS IN BIKINI LAGOON SUP-
PLIED BY JOINT ARMY-NAVY TASK FORCE ONE)

PART ONE

Genesis

CHAPTER ONE

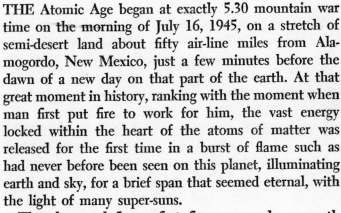

THE Atomic Age began at exactly 5.30 mountain war time on the morning of July 16, 1945, on a stretch of semi-desert land about fifty air-line miles from Alamogordo, New Mexico, just a few minutes before the dawn of a new day on that part of the earth. At that great moment in history, ranking with the moment when man first put fire to work for him, the vast energy locked within the heart of the atoms of matter was released for the first time in a burst of flame such as had never before been seen on this planet, illuminating earth and sky, for a brief span that seemed eternal, with the light of many super-suns.

The elemental flame, first fire ever made on earth that did not have its origin in the sun, came from the explosion of the first atomic bomb. It was a full-dress rehearsal preparatory to dropping the bomb over Hiroshima and Nagasaki—and other Japanese military targets, had Japan refused to accept the Potsdam Declaration for her surrender.

The rehearsal marked the climax in the penultimate act of one of the greatest dramas in our history and the history of civilized man—a drama in which our scientists, under the direction of the Army Corps of Engineers, were working against time to create an atomic

3

bomb ahead of our German enemy. The collapse of Germany marked the end of the first act of this drama. The successful completion of our task, in the greatest challenge by man to nature so far, brought down the curtain on the second act. The grand finale came three weeks afterward in the skies over Japan, with a swift descent of the curtain on the greatest war in history.

The atomic flash in New Mexico came as a great affirmation to the prodigious labors of our scientists during the past four years. It came as the affirmative answer to the until then unanswered question: "Will it work?"

With the flash came a delayed roll of mighty thunder, heard, just as the flash was seen, for hundreds of miles. The roar echoed and reverberated from the distant hills and the Sierra Oscuro range near by, sounding as though it came from some supramundane source as well as from the bowels of the earth. The hills said yes and the mountains chimed in yes. It was as if the earth had spoken and the suddenly iridescent clouds and sky had joined in one affirmative answer. Atomic energy—yes. It was like the grand finale of a mighty symphony of the elements, fascinating and terrifying, uplifting and crushing, ominous, devastating, full of great promise and great forebodings.

I watched the birth of the era of atomic power from the slope of a hill in the desert land of New Mexico, on the northwestern corner of the Alamogordo Air Base, about 125 miles southeast of Albuquerque. The hill, named Compania Hill for the occasion, was twenty miles to the northwest of Zero, the code name given to the spot chosen for the atomic bomb test. The area embracing Zero and Compania Hill, twenty-four miles long and eighteen miles wide, had the code name Trinity.

4

I joined a caravan of three busses, three automobiles, and a truck carrying radio equipment at 11 p.m. on Sunday, July 15, at Albuquerque. There were about ninety of us in that strange caravan, traveling silently and in the utmost secrecy through the night on probably as unusual an adventure as any in our day. With the exception of myself the caravan consisted of scientists from the highly secret atomic bomb research and development center in the mesas and canyons of New Mexico, twenty-five miles northwest of Santa Fe, where we solved the secret of translating the fabulous energy of the atom into the mightiest weapon ever made by man. It was from there that the caravan set out at 5.30 that Sunday afternoon for its destination, 212 miles to the south.

The caravan wound its way slowly over the tortuous roads overlooking the precipitous canyons of northern New Mexico, passing through Espagnola, Santa Fe, and Bernalillo, arriving at Albuquerque at about 10 p.m. Here it was joined by Sir James Chadwick, who won the Nobel Prize and knighthood for his discovery of the neutron, the key that unlocks the atom; Professor Ernest O. Lawrence of the University of California, master atom-smasher, who won the Nobel Prize for his discovery of the cyclotron; Professor Edwin M. McMillan, also of the University of California, one of the discoverers of plutonium, the new atomic energy element; and several others from the atomic bomb center, who, like me, had arrived during the afternoon.

The night was dark with black clouds, and not a star could be seen. Occasionally a bolt of lightning would rend the sky and reveal for an instant the flat semi-desert landscape, rich with historic lore of past adventure. We rolled along on U. S. Highway 85, running between Albuquerque and El Paso, through sleeping

5

ancient Spanish-American towns, their windows dark, their streets deserted—towns with music in their names, Los Lunas, Belen, Bernardo, Alamillo, Socorro, San Antonio. At San Antonio we turned east and crossed "the bridge on the Rio Grande with the detour in the middle of it." From there we traveled ten and one half miles eastward on U. S. Highway 380, and then turned south on a specially built dirt road, running for twenty-five miles to the base camp at Trinity.

The end of our trail was reached after we had covered about five and one fifth miles on the dirt road. Here we saw the first signs of life since leaving Albuquerque about three hours earlier, a line of silent men dressed in helmets. A little farther on, a detachment of military police examined our special credentials. We got out of the busses and looked around us. The night was still pitch-black save for an occasional flash of lightning in the eastern sky, outlining for a brief instant the Sierra Oscuro Range directly ahead of us. We were in the middle of the New Mexico desert, miles away from nowhere, with hardly a sign of life, not even a blinking light on the distant horizon. This was to be our caravansary until the zero hour.

From a distance to the southeast the beam of a searchlight probed the clouds. This gave us our first sense of orientation. The bomb-test site, Zero, was a little to the left of the searchlight beam, twenty miles away. With the darkness and the waiting in the chill of the desert the tension became almost unendurable.

We gathered in a circle to listen to directions on what we were to do at the time of the test, directions read aloud by the light of a flashlight:

At a short signal of the siren at minus five minutes to zero, "all personnel whose duties did not specifically

6

require otherwise" were to prepare "a suitable place to lie down on." At a long signal of the siren at minus two minutes to zero, "all personnel whose duties did not specifically require otherwise" were to "lie prone on the ground immediately, the face and eyes directed toward the ground and with the head away from Zero. Do not watch for the flash directly," the directions read, "but turn over after it has occurred and watch the cloud. Stay on the ground until the blast wave has passed (two minutes). At two short blasts of the siren, indicating the passing of all hazard from light and blast, all personnel will prepare to leave as soon as possible.

"The hazard from blast is reduced by lying down on the ground in such a manner that flying rocks, glass and other objects do not intervene between the source of blast and the individual. Open all car windows.

"The hazard from light injury to eyes is reduced by shielding the closed eyes with the bended arms and lying face down on the ground. If the first flash is viewed a 'blind spot' may prevent your seeing the rest of the show.

"The hazard from ultraviolet light injuries to the skin is best overcome by wearing long trousers and shirts with long sleeves."

David Dow, assistant to the scientific director of the Atomic Bomb Development Center, handed each of us a flat piece of colored glass such as is used by arc welders to shield their eyes. Dr. Edward Teller of George Washington University cautioned us against sunburn. Someone produced sunburn lotion and passed it around. It was an eerie sight to see a number of our highest-ranking scientists seriously rubbing sunburn lotion on their faces and hands in the pitch-blackness of the night, twenty miles away from the expected flash. These were

7

the men who, more than anybody else, knew the potentialities of atomic energy on the loose. It gave one an inkling of their confidence in their handiwork.

The bomb was set on a structural steel tower one hundred feet high. Ten miles away to the southwest was the base camp. This was G.H.Q. for the scientific high command, of which Professor Kenneth T. Bainbridge of Harvard University was field commander. Here were erected barracks to serve as living-quarters for the scientists, a mess hall, a commissary, a post exchange, and other buildings. Here the vanguard of the atomists, headed by Professor J. R. Oppenheimer of the University of California, scientific director of the Atomic Bomb Project, lived like soldiers at the front, supervising the enormously complicated details involved in the epoch-making tests.

Here early that Sunday afternoon gathered Major General Leslie R. Groves, commander in chief of the Atomic Bomb Project; Brigadier General T. F. Farrell, hero of World War I, General Groves's deputy; Professor Enrico Fermi, Nobel prize winner and one of the leaders in the project; President James Bryant Conant of Harvard; Dr. Vannevar Bush, director of the Office of Scientific Research and Development; Dean Richard C. Tolman of the California Institute of Technology; Professor R. F. Bacher of Cornell; Colonel Stafford L. Warren, University of Rochester radiologist; and about a hundred and fifty other leaders in the atomic bomb program.

At the Base Camp was a dry, abandoned reservoir, about five hundred feet square, surrounded by a mound of earth about eight feet high. Within this mound bulldozers dug a series of slit trenches, each about three feet deep, seven feet wide, and twenty-five feet long. At a command over the radio at zero minus one minute all

8

observers at Base Camp, lay down in their assigned trenches, "face and eyes directed toward the ground and with the head away from Zero." But most of us on Compania Hill remained on our feet.

Three other posts had been established, south, north, and west of Zero, each at a distance of 10,000 yards (5.7 miles). These were known, respectively, as South-10,000, North-10,000, and West-10,000, or S-10, N-10, and W-10. Here the shelters were much more elaborate —wooden structures, their walls reinforced by cement, buried under a massive layer of earth.

S-10 was the control center. Here Professor Oppenheimer, as scientific commander in chief, and his field commander, Professor Bainbridge, issued orders and synchronized the activities af the other sites. Here the signal was given and a complex of mechanisms was set in motion that resulted in the greatest burst of energy ever released by man on earth up to that time. No switch was pulled, no button pressed, to light this first cosmic fire on this planet.

At forty-five seconds to zero, set for 5.30 o'clock, young Dr. Joseph L. McKibben of the University of California, at a signal from Professor Bainbridge, activated a master robot that set off a series of other robots, until, at last, strategically spaced electrons moved to the proper place at the proper split second.

Forty-five seconds passed and the moment was zero.

Meanwhile at our observation post on Compania Hill the atmosphere had grown tenser as the zero hour approached. We had spent the first part of our stay eating an early morning picnic breakfast that we had taken along with us. It had grown cold in the desert, and many of us, lightly clad, shivered. Occasionally a drizzle came down, and the intermittent flashes of lightning made us turn apprehensive glances toward Zero. We had had some disturbing reports that the test might be called off because of the weather. The radio we had brought with us for communication with Base Camp kept going out of order, and when we had finally repaired it some blatant band would drown out the news we wanted to hear. We knew there were two specially equipped B-29 Superfortresses high over head to make observations and recordings in the upper atmosphere, but we could neither see nor hear them. We kept gazing through the blackness.

Suddenly, at 5.29.50, as we stood huddled around our radio, we heard a voice ringing through the darkness, sounding as though it had come from above the clouds: "Zero minus ten seconds!" A green flare flashed out through the clouds, descended slowly, opened, grew dim, and vanished into the darkness.

The voice from the clouds boomed out again: "Zero minus three seconds!" Another green flare came down. Silence reigned over the desert. We kept moving in small groups in the direction of Zero. From the east came the first faint signs of dawn.

And just at that instant there rose from the bowels of the earth a light not of this world, the light of many suns in one. It was a sunrise such as the world had never seen, a great green super-sun climbing in a fraction of a second to a height of more than eight thousand feet, rising ever higher until it touched the clouds, lighting up earth and sky all around with a dazzling luminosity.

Up it went, a great ball of fire about a mile in diameter, changing colors as it kept shooting upward, from deep purple to orange, expanding, growing bigger, rising as it expanded, an elemental force freed from its bonds after being chained for billions of years. For a fleeting instant the color was unearthly green, such as one sees only in the corona of the sun during a total eclipse. It

10

was as though the earth had opened and the skies had split. One felt as though one were present at the moment of creation when God said: "Let there be light."

To another observer, Professor George B. Kistiakowsky of Harvard, the spectacle was "the nearest thing to doomsday that one could possibly imagine. I am sure," he said, "that at the end of the world—in the last millisecond of the earth's existence—the last man will see what we have just seen!"

A great cloud rose from the ground and followed the trail of the great sun. At first it was a giant column, which soon took the shape of a supramundane mushroom. For a fleeting instant it took the form of the Statue of Liberty magnified many times. Up it went, higher, higher, a giant mountain born in a few seconds instead of millions of years, quivering convulsively. It touched the multicolored clouds, pushed its summit through them, kept rising until it reached a height of 41,000 feet, 12,000 feet higher than the earth's highest mountain.

All through this very short but extremely long time-interval not a sound was heard. I could see the silhouettes of human forms motionless in little groups, like desert plants in the dark. The newborn mountain in the distance, a giant among the pygmies of the Sierra Oscuro Range, stood leaning at an angle against the clouds, a vibrant volcano spouting fire to the sky.

Then out of the great silence came a mighty thunder. For a brief interval the phenomena we had seen as light repeated themselves in terms of sound. It was the blast from thousands of blockbusters going off simultaneously at one spot. The thunder reverberated all through the desert, bounced back and forth from the Sierra Oscuro, echo upon echo. The ground trembled under our feet as in an earthquake. A wave of hot wind was felt by many of us just before the blast and warned us of its coming.

The big boom came about one hundred seconds after the great flash—the first cry of a newborn world. It brought the silent, motionless silhouettes to life, gave them a voice. A loud cry filled the air. The little groups that had hitherto stood rooted to the earth like desert plants broke into a dance—the rhythm of primitive man dancing at one of his fire festivals at the coming of spring. They clapped their hands as they leaped from the ground—earthbound man symbolizing the birth of a new force that for the first time gives man means to free himself from the gravitational pull of the earth that holds him down.

The dance of the primitive man lasted but a few seconds, during which an evolutionary period of about 10,000 years had been telescoped. Primitive man was metamorphosed into modern man—shaking hands, slapping his fellow on the back, all laughing like happy children.

The sun was just rising above the horizon as our caravan started on its way back to Albuquerque and Los Alamos. We looked at it through our dark lenses to compare it with what we had seen.

"The sun can't hold a candle to it!" one of us remarked.

CHAPTER TWO

IN that infinitesimal fraction of time, inconceivable and immeasurable, during which the first atomic bomb converted a small part of its matter into the greatest burst of energy released on earth up to that time, Prometheus had broken his bonds and brought a new fire down to earth, a fire three million times more powerful than the original fire he snatched from the gods for the benefit of man some five hundred thousand years ago.

Civilization as we know it has thrived until now on that original spark kindled by Prometheus. That fire, no matter in what form it is used, has its original source in the sun. When we burn wood, we use solar energy bottled up by the tree during the process of its growth. When we eat plants to get the energy for living, we utilize the sun's energy trapped by the plant. When we burn coal or oil to produce heat or power, whether mechanical or electrical, we again take advantage of solar energy stored up in plants millions of years ago, for both coal and oil are but petrified vegetable matter that gathered up the sunlight of long ago, before man made his appearance on earth. The power of wind and of water is the direct result of solar heat, for water would freeze and the air would not circulate were it not for the sun.

But there is another type of energy known on earth

13

that does not have its origin in the sun. This is the energy emanating from substances such as radium, uranium, and similar heavy elements, known as radioactivity. It is the discovery of these elements about fifty years ago that led step by step to the development of the atomic bomb. The discovery of these radioactive elements brought about a complete revolution in our concepts of the two fundamental entities of our cosmos —matter and energy. Every schoolboy had been taught, and is still being taught, as eternal verities, that matter can be neither created nor destroyed, but only altered in form, and similarly that energy can be neither created nor destroyed, but only altered in form. These are known, respectively, as the law of the conservation of mass and the law of the conservation of energy. The explosion of the atomic bomb in New Mexico demonstrated on a large scale what the discovery of the radioactive substances had already done on a small scale: namely, that matter and energy are but two manifestations of a single principle, and that matter and energy can be both created and destroyed in the sense that each can be converted into the other.

When the atomic bombs exploded over New Mexico and Japan, a sizable amount of what we call matter definitely disappeared from the cosmos and transformed itself into pure energy. There was less matter in the world after these explosions. The law of conservation of mass and the law of conservation of energy were, in a sense, blown up by the atomic bomb as were the steel tower in New Mexico and the cities of Hiroshima and Nagasaki. It is still true, of course, that neither matter nor energy can be destroyed in the sense of being completely annihilated. But since we know that matter can be transformed into energy, and vice versa, it is no

14

longer true that matter always remains matter, and energy always remains energy.

We must, moreover, change our concepts of matter and energy even in their ordinary manifestations. For example, it is still commonly believed that when we burn a piece of coal, the weight of the ashes and the gaseous products evolved would be exactly the same as that of the original piece of coal. For all practical purposes this is still true, but only because the actual amount of matter in the coal that is converted into energy, in the form of heat and light, is so infinitesimal that we have no means for determining it. By comparing the amount of heat liberated with the much greater amounts of heat liberated from radium, for example, we know exactly how much of the coal substance has been converted into energy, since Einstein, in his theory of relativity, has provided us with a formula for the amount of energy equivalent to a given amount of matter. But so far we have not been able to demonstrate experimentally the actual loss of matter in ordinary types of combustion, in which only molecular energy is liberated.

Through the Einstein formula, the correctness of which has been proved again and again by measuring the energy emanating from radioactive substances and comparing it with the corresponding loss of mass in these substances, as well as by other methods, we now know that one gram of matter, four tenths the weight of a dime, if converted entirely into energy, would yield 25,-000,000 kilowatt-hours, about three billion times the energy that is liberated in the burning of an equal amount of coal. The burning of one gram of coal would therefore entail the loss of one third of a billionth of a gram, an amount too small to be measured by present means at our disposal.

What accounts for this vast difference between the energy contained in matter and its actual yield in ordinary processes of combustion, such as the burning of coal or oil? The answer is to be found in the fundamental structure of matter. The material universe, until the advent of the atomic bomb, consisted of ninety-two natural elements, such as hydrogen, carbon, nitrogen, oxygen, iron, copper, silver, gold, platinum, mercury, and many other common, or relatively rare, natural substances. The smallest unit of any of these ninety-two elements—that is, the unit beyond which it can not be further divided without losing its identity—is known as the atom of that particular element. Two or more atoms of the same element, or two or more atoms of different elements, held together by chemical forces, are known as molecules. For example, two atoms of hydrogen and one atom of oxygen unite chemically to form one molecule of water. One atom of sodium and one atom of chlorine unite chemically to form one molecule of table salt.

The atoms in their turn are not the simple solid substances they were thought to be less than fifty years ago. They are now conceived of as extremely minute solar systems, with a heavy central core, or nucleus, surrounded by much lighter particles that revolve about the central nucleus as the planets revolve around the sun. The central nucleus is from two thousand to five thousand times heavier than its surrounding "planets"; in other words, 99.98 per cent of the matter of our cosmos is concentrated in the central nucleus of the atoms of the ninety-two basic elements.

Since matter is equivalent to energy, it can be readily seen that nearly all the energy in the universe is concentrated within the atomic nucleus.

Now, the nucleus is nature's most formidable citadel.

16

It is surrounded by a barrier of such inconceivable magnitude that no force at man's disposal, until the atomic bomb, was sufficient to make any appreciable dent in it. As Sir Arthur Eddington said in 1930, it was, the "cosmic cupboard," the key to which nature had successfully hidden from man. All the energy at his disposal, that which he obtained through the bounty of the sun, in the combustion of fuels, in ordinary explosions, and through other chemical processes, could come only from the energy liberated when atoms share between themselves the "planets" that form the outer portion of an atom's structure, which contain no more than two hundredths of one per cent of the total energy within the atom. In fact, he could get only a small fraction of that two hundredths of one per cent, since only the outermost "planets," those few in the outside orbits farthest away from the nucleus, are involved in ordinary chemical reactions. The nucleus of the atom is in no way affected by these processes.

The "planets" surrounding the nuclei of the atoms are known as electrons, exceedingly minute fundamental particles of matter, carrying a basic unit of negative electricity. Since their discovery in 1897 by J. J. Thomson they have brought about the modern age of electronics. They have made possible radio, television, talking motion pictures, the transatlantic telephone, thousands of automatic industrial processes. Long before their identity was even suspected—in fact, since the beginning of time—they have made possible man's existence on earth, for all life is a chemical process and all chemical processes, as we have seen, are carried on by the outermost electrons in the planetary orbits around the nuclei of the atoms. When Prometheus taught man the use of fire he was, without knowing it, teaching man how to liberate the molecular energy bound up in the electrons.

17

Of all the atoms, the simplest is the hydrogen atom. It has only one electron, which revolves planet-like around the nucleus. This nucleus consists of one proton, another fundamental atomic particle, 1,836 times heavier than the electron. The proton carries a fundamental unit of positive electricity of exactly the same magnitude as the electron, so that the two balance each other electrically, making the atom electrically neutral.

Nature built up her ninety-two elements with beautiful simplicity, in the manner of a child placing one block on top of another. All she did was to add one proton to the nucleus of hydrogen and, presto, there was the next element, helium. She added one proton to helium and there was her third element, lithium. Step by step, one proton at a time, she thus built up her elements until she stopped at element No. 92, uranium, which, until the advent of the atomic bomb, was the heaviest element in nature.

The number of protons in the nucleus determines the number of electrons in the various planet-like orbits in the relatively vast outer spaces of the atoms; and the outermost electrons, in their turn, determine the chemical properties of the atoms. Since each proton has one definite unit of electric charge, the nature of each element depends on the number of these units.

The number of positive electric charges in the nucleus —namely, the number of protons—is known as the atomic number. Thus hydrogen stands at atomic No. 1 in the periodic table of elements. Helium, with two protons in its nucleus, stands at No. 2; lithium at No. 3. Carbon, with six protons in its nucleus, stands at No. 6, nitrogen at No. 7, oxygen at No. 8, and so on through the entire list of natural elements, up to uranium, which stands at atomic No. 92, meaning that its nucleus contains ninety-two fundamental units of positive electricity —in other words, ninety-two protons.

This enables us to understand why the alchemists failed in their efforts to transmute the elements. The only way this could be done would be to change the atomic number of an element by adding to or subtracting from the fixed number of its protons. This, as explained earlier, requires forces great enough to overcome the tremendous electrical barrier surrounding the nucleus, forces that had not been available to man until now.

Gold has the atomic number 79, as its nucleus contains seventy-nine protons. Mercury has the atomic number 80. Thus if one could knock one proton out of the nucleus of mercury one would realize the alchemist's dream. While this has been done on a very small scale, we still do not know of a practical way of doing it.

There is a third fundamental building block of nature, which, from the point of view of the atomic bomb and atomic power in general, is the most important. It was discovered in 1932 by Professor Chadwick, of Cambridge University, and caused one of the greatest revolutions in man's history, with implications so vast that it will take many years, possibly several generations, to assess its full significance. This particle was named the neutron. As its name implies, it is electrically neutral. It has a mass almost the same as that of the proton. It possesses tremendous energy. Its habitat is inside the nucleus of the atoms.

The total number of protons and neutrons in the nucleus determines the atomic mass, as distinguished from the atomic number. Thus carbon stands at atomic number 6 on the periodic table of the elements, but has an atomic mass of 12. This means that, in addition to

19

six protons, it also contains six neutrons. By subtracting the atomic number (that is, the number of protons) from the atomic mass, the number of neutrons in the nucleus of each element can be determined.

Elements that have the same atomic number but different atomic masses are known as isotopes. For example, hydrogen has three isotopes of atomic masses 1, 2, and 3, respectively. They all contain one proton in the nucleus. But the first contains no neutrons (the only element of its kind), the second contains one neutron, and the third, two.

Elements that have the same atomic mass but different atomic numbers are known as isobars. For example, there is a rare form of helium of atomic mass 3. It thus has the same mass as hydrogen 3, but whereas the nucleus of the latter contains one proton and two neutrons, that of the former contains two protons and one neutron.

It is the neutron that provided us with the key to the cosmic store of power in the nucleus of uranium, nature's heaviest atom, and holds out the promise of tapping the energy in the nuclei of other atoms. It is again the neutron that served as the trigger in the atomic bomb. It is the long-sought philosophers' stone, with which man has created many new elements more precious than gold. With it more concentrated power has been liberated than ever before in history, but even that is only a trickle compared with the promise of things to come. Used properly, it gives man the means for realizing the dream of the ages. With it he can shatter his world to bits "and then remould it nearer to the Heart's Desire." Or he can just shatter it to bits.

The neutron possesses this power just because it is electrically neutral, which makes possible its use as a projectile into the nuclei of atoms. All other atomic particles available for such purposes, such as protons and electrons, are stopped from penetrating into the nucleus of atoms by the tremendous electrical wall surrounding it. The neutron, possessing no electrical charge, can slip right through that barrier.

Penetrating the nucleus! That was the key science had been looking for, the key that nature had hidden from man since the beginning of time. For to tap the vast cosmic storehouse of power within the nucleus man needed a cosmic bullet with which to split it open. All other atomic bullets he had until then bounced right back off the electrical wall. The neutron bounced right in.

It was the sword with which to open the cosmic oyster.

Atomic energy, harnessed for the first time by our scientists for use in atomic bombs, is the practically inexhaustible source of power that enables our sun to supply us with heat, light, and other forms of radiant energy, without which life on earth would not be possible. It is the same energy, stored in the nuclei of the atoms of the material universe, that keeps the stars, bodies much larger than our sun, radiating their enormous quantities of light and heat for billions of years instead of burning themselves out in periods measured only in thousands of years.

The existence of atomic energy was first discovered by Einstein about forty years ago on purely theoretical grounds, as an outgrowth of his famous theory of relativity, according to which a body in motion has a greater mass than the same body at rest, this increase in mass bearing a direct relationship to the velocity of light. This meant that the energy of motion imparts an actual increase in mass.

From the formula for the relationship of this increase

21

of mass to the velocity of light Einstein derived his famous mathematical equation that revealed for the first time an equivalence between mass and energy, one of the most revolutionary concepts in the intellectual history of mankind. The mass-energy equation showed that any given quantity of mass is the equivalent of a specific amount of energy, and vice versa.

Specifically this equation revealed the fact, incredible at that time, that very small amounts of matter contain tremendous amounts of energy. A piece of coal the size of a pea, the equation proved, contains enough energy to drive the largest ocean liner across the Atlantic and back. No one, however, least of all Einstein himself, believed at that time that any means could ever be found to tap this cosmic source of elemental energy.

In the mass-energy theorem Einstein showed the existence of a definite relationship between the cosmic trinity of matter, energy, and the velocity of light. The relationship is so simple that, once arrived at, a grammar-school student could work it out. In this formula the letter m stands for mass in terms of grams; the letter E represents energy in terms of ergs (a small unit of energy or work); the letter c stands for the velocity of light in terms of centimeters per second. The energy content of any given quantity of any substance, the formula states, is equal to the mass of the substance (in terms of grams) multiplied by the square of the velocity of light (in terms of centimeters per second). The velocity of light (in round numbers) is 300,000 kilometers, or 30,-000,000,000 centimeters, per second.

Take one gram of any substance. According to the Einstein formula, the amount of energy (E) in ergs in this mass is equal to 1 (the mass of the substance in grams) multiplied by 30,000,000,000 squared. In other words, the energy content of one gram of matter equals

900 billion billion ergs. Translated into terms of pounds and kilowatt-hours, this means that one pound of matter contains the energy equivalent of 10,000,000,000 kilowatt-hours.

If this energy could be fully utilized, it would take only twenty-two pounds of matter to supply all the electrical power requirements of the United States for a year. One third of a gram of water would yield enough heat to turn 12,000 tons of water into steam. One gram of water would raise a load of a million tons to the top of a mountain six miles high. A breath of air would operate a powerful airplane continuously for a year. A handful of snow would heat a large apartment house for a year. The pasteboard in a small railroad ticket would run a heavy passenger train several times around the world. A cup of water would supply the power of a great generating station of 100,000-kilowatt capacity for six years.

One pound of any substance, if its atomic-energy content could be utilized one hundred per cent, is equivalent in power content to 3,000,000,000 pounds of coal, or 1,500,000 tons. The energy we are now able to utilize in the atomic bombs, at maximum efficiency, constitutes only one tenth of one per cent of the total energy present in the material. But even one hundredth of one per cent would still be by far the most destructive force on this earth.

Atomic energy, released through the splitting of atoms, differs radically from ordinary types of energy hitherto available to man in that it involves a fundamental change in the nature of the atom, a change in which an appreciable amount of matter is converted into energy.

This is materially different from obtaining power by the use of a water wheel, for example, or by the burning of coal or oil. In the case of the water wheel, the water molecules taking part remain entirely unchanged. They simply lose potential energy as they pass from the dam to the tailrace. In the case of burning coal or oil a more intense process takes place, as the atoms of carbon, hydrogen, and oxygen (of which the coal and oil molecules are composed) are regrouped by combustion into new molecules forming new substances. The atoms themselves, however, still remain unchanged—they still are carbon, hydrogen, and oxygen. None of them, so far as can be measured, loses any part of its mass.

In the case of atomic energy, however, the atom itself completely changes its identity, and in this process of change it loses part of its mass, which is converted into energy. The amount of energy liberated in this process is directly proportional to the amount of atomic mass destroyed.

The sun, for example, obtains its energy through the partial destruction of its hydrogen, through a complex process in which the hydrogen is converted into helium. In this process four hydrogen atoms, each with an atomic mass of 1.008 (total, 4.032 atomic mass units) combine to form one helium atom, which has an atomic mass of 4.003. This represents a loss of mass in the four hydrogen atoms (in addition to a loss of two positive electrons) of 0.029 atomic mass units, which is coverted into pure energy. The amount of energy liberated in this process by the enormous quantities of hydrogen in the sun represents an actual loss of the sun's mass at the rate of 4,000,-000 tons per second, a mere speck of dust in relation to the sun's total mass of two billion billion billion tons.

If the sun, however, were a mass of coal weighing the same amount, it would have to burn three billion times the mass it is burning now to produce the same amount of energy. If that were the case, it would have used up

24

the entire store of molecular energy contained in its body of coal in the course of 5,750 years. In other words, it would have burned out long before the earth was born.

By the use of atomic energy the sun has been able to give off its enormous amounts of radiation for a period estimated at 10 billion years, and its mass, at the present rate of burning, is enough to last 15,000 billion years more, although, of course, the amount of its radiation would be greatly reduced long before that in proportion to the decrease of its mass. Radiations in amounts sufficient to support life on earth are estimated to continue for some ten billion to a hundred billion years longer.

Since the very existence of atomic energy was first discovered through the theory of relativity, the development of the atomic bomb constitutes the most dramatic proof so far offered for the correctness of the theory, and also marks the first time it has been put to practical use in mundane affairs.

It is one of the great ironies of history that the German war lords, who drove Einstein into exile, were forced to rely on the theory of relativity in their efforts to develop an atomic bomb to save them from defeat. The United States, of which Einstein is now an honored citizen, succeeded where the Nazis failed. When the bombs fell over Hiroshima and Nagasaki, they represented the fruition of what had been originally a pure mathematical concept. Had that concept not come when it did, the development of the atomic bomb might also have had to wait. This might have meant a prolongation of the war. Thousands of young Americans thus may owe their lives to the theory of relativity—which is another way of saying that pure science, no matter how impractical it may appear, pays high dividends in the end.

25

CHAPTER THREE

I HAD the privilege of spending the entire day on Sunday, July 15, 1945, and all those hours up to 5.30 of the morning of July 16, in the company of Professor Chadwick. I rode with him on the first leg of our journey from Los Alamos to Albuquerque, where we spent the day waiting for the rest of our caravan. I stood next to him when the great moment for the neutron arrived. Never before in history had any man lived to see his own discovery materialize itself with such telling effect on the destiny of man, for the immediate present and all the generations to come. The infinitesimal neutron, to which the world paid little attention when its discovery was first announced, had cast its shadow over the entire earth and its inhabitants. On that ride, as I sat there beside the neutron's discoverer, this shadow sat between us. We conversed with it, largely through silences interrupted here and there by words.

He became more silent as the agonizing hours dragged on, and as the zero hour approached, I saw him standing there alone, looking off to the east, in the manner of a man awaiting a new apocalypse. As the great moment came and the primitive pandemonium broke all around him, he was still standing there, rooted to the earth, looking (to use the phrase of Dr. Charles A. Thomas)

26

"very inanimate." Then a human spirit, electrified by the great burst of neutrons, actuated a hand and made it descend with a resounding slap on Dr. Chadwick's slight back. He grunted, leaped lightly into the air, and was still again.

A few miles to the east of us, in a lead-lined Sherman tank, sat Dr. Fermi, riding in the new no-man's-land, scorched as no earth had ever been scorched before. He was measuring the radiations on the surface of this newly created jadelike earth, the ocean of invisible light that had just been liberated by the neutrons.

To Dr. Chadwick and Dr. Fermi, more than to any other men present that morning in the New Mexico desert, the great burst of light and the earth's thunder represented a consummation, the greatest materialization ever granted to a mortal of what had started as a pure idea. For the light and the thunder were both the result of the neutron cracking open the atom of uranium, or the atoms of an element derived from uranium, and Dr. Fermi had been the first to shoot neutrons at uranium atoms, and the first to create new elements beyond uranium.

The story began at the University of Rome in 1934, when Dr. Fermi was thirty-three years old. He and his colleagues had been industriously bombarding most of the elements with neutrons as projectiles and observed many strange Alice-Through-the-Looking-Glass events. As was expected, the neutron, because it has no electric charge, penetrated the barrier of the nucleus and frequently lodged there. Since the neutron is about equal in mass to the proton, the addition of one neutron meant an increase in the atomic weight of the element by one unit. But the elements in which the neutrons lodged, or, as the physicists say, the nuclei that captured a neutron, became unbalanced because the extra neutron gave them

27

more energy than they could hold. To regain their stability, the nuclei began throwing off that extra energy in the form of radiations.

Here came surprise number one. The radiations came out in the form of electrons, particles with a negative charge of electricity. But by that time it had been established that the nucleus consisted of only protons and neutrons. There are no electrons as such in the nucleus. Where could these electrons have come from?

Then came surprise number two. On examining the elements bombarded with the neutrons it was found that many of them were no longer the same elements, as their nuclei contained an extra proton. Where could this proton have come from?

There could be only one logical explanation of both mysteries. Both the electron and the proton came from the neutron. At least some neutrons, if not all, these experiments seemed to indicate, are in a state of electrical neutrality because they carry both a positive and a negative electrical charge, which balance each other. Under certain conditions a neutron could be made to vibrate so violently that its electron was broken off and bounced out of the nucleus. This left the neutron positively charged; in other words, it became a proton.

If that is the case, Fermi reasoned, what would happen if a neutron were fired into the nucleus of a uranium atom? Uranium is the last and heaviest element made by nature. It has 92 protons and 146 neutrons in its nucleus, with a total atomic weight of 238. The shooting of an extra neutron into its nucleus would raise its atomic weight to 239. But if one of its neutrons parted with its electron, it would become a proton, and the nucleus would have 93 instead of 92 protons. That would mean the creation of an entirely new element.

Scientists are supposedly individuals who leave their

28

emotions behind when they enter their laboratories, but that day when Dr. Fermi and his associates, all young men, first fired neutrons at uranium was tense with expectations and high hopes. It was an adventure into the ultimate, a journey to a hitherto unknown continent of matter, bound to push back the frontiers of knowledge no matter what happened.

What they were actually doing, without knowing it, was making miniature atomic bombs. For that is what the atomic bomb is—a species of uranium, or uranium derivative, violently exploded by an avalanche of neutrons. They were also building a model atomic power plant, for the explosion of that species of uranium, whose existence was not known at the time though it was present in the samples of uranium they were using, is accompanied by the liberation of enormous amounts of atomic energy. Without knowing it, they were even laying the foundation for controlling the atomic power plant of the future, for by that time Dr. Fermi had developed the method of taming the neutron by slowing it down, a method essential for producing atomic power under control. But none of them even remotely suspected any of this at the time, and, as was learned later, it was well that nature kept her secret a little while longer.

Like Columbus these young pioneers discovered a great deal more than they had set out to find, and like him they were unaware of the vastness and riches of the new continent they had opened up. But what they did find, and other things they believed at the time they had found, created one of the greatest scientific sensations of the day. It made the name of Enrico Fermi internationally known and won for him the Nobel prize for physics in 1938.

The results they observed far exceeded even their

most optimistic expectations. The neutrons fired at element 92 seemed to produce not only element 93 but, strange to behold, also element 94. Though this was somewhat more than they had bargained for, it fitted well into the scheme of things.

But then something seemed to go berserk, as though old Mother Nature had gone on a mad spree. For closer examination revealed that the mating of neutrons with uranium had given birth to at least a score of "illegitimate" substances that came popping out like genii from a magic bottle. It was as though an elemental bull had gone wild in the cosmic china shop. For a time it was believed that three of these "illegitimates" might be elements 95, 96, and 97, but it soon became evident that none of them could be fitted properly into any spot in the restricted spaces of the periodic table in the vicinity of uranium, where they properly belonged if they were really elements beyond uranium. And, according to the best knowledge available at the time, they could not be anything else.

Actually, as was learned five years later, they were the fragments of uranium atoms that had been split by the neutrons, forming radioactive varieties of "legitimate" elements much lighter than uranium, and occupying spots 36 to 56 spaces farther back than uranium in the periodic table. But that was too revolutionary a concept even to think about in the antediluvian period of the atomic age, *A.D.* 1934.

The transuranium elements born through the fertilization of uranium with neutrons became the most tantalizing mystery among atom-smashers the world over. For five years all the major nuclear physics laboratories in many lands worked on its solution. And the mystery seemed to grow more profound as more facts came to the surface.

30

The stage for the final solution of the mystery was not set until the autumn of 1938, at about the time of the Pact of Munich. The scene was the Kaiser Wilhelm Institute in Berlin. The dramatis personæ: Otto Hahn, Fritz Strassmann, and Lise Meitner. By that time methods had been worked out for the chemical analysis of the minute bits of matter produced by modern alchemy in the course of transmuting one atomic nucleus into another or in the creation of artificially radioactive elements. Drs. Hahn, Strassmann, and Meitner began by repeating the original Fermi experiment, bombarding uranium with neutrons. With the new technique for analyzing the products of such bombardment they proceeded on the tedious, and until then fruitless, task of identifying the mysterious substance for which no proper home could be found in the infinite cosmos.

At last there was a glimmer of hope, a ray of recognition. One of the illegitimate offspring of the uranium-neutron union gave off gamma rays very similar to those of radium, though much more powerful. One way in which this could happen would be if the neutron caused the bombarded uranium atom to emit two alpha particles, or a total of four protons and four neutrons. This would mean an unheard-of phenomenon—that the original uranium nucleus had lost four of its 92 protons and four of its 146 neutrons, leaving a nucleus of 88 protons and 142 neutrons, or four more neutrons than the normal radium nucleus. These four extra neutrons would make the nucleus much more unstable and would account for its radioactivity being greater than that of normal radium.

Now, to separate radium from other elements the normal procedure is through the addition of barium, element No. 56. The barium combines chemically with the radium in the mixture of other substances and carries

31

it down with it in the form of a precipitate. The radium-barium precipitate is then separated from the solution, and the barium is then in turn separated from the radium by a specific chemical process. The Hahn-Strassmann-Meitner team therefore proceeded in the usual way to isolate the substance they believed to be a new form of radium by adding barium to the mixture of strange uranium progeny. As they had expected, the barium combined with the new radium-like substance and precipitated it out of the solution containing the other substances.

But when they came to separate the "radium" from the barium by the usual standard methods, they had the surprise of their scientific lives—in fact, one of the greatest surprises in the entire history of science. For the barium refused to be separated from the so-called "radium" by any method known to chemistry. The two clung together in an indissoluble union.

There could be only one inescapable conclusion. The fact that the barium could not be separated could mean only that the mysterious substance that had been believed to be a form of radium could not be anything but barium, a radioactive barium that had been present before they added the normal barium to serve as the carrier. They had believed they were about to solve a mystery and found themselves confronted with an even greater mystery. Where could this super-radioactive barium have come from? It was like observing a chicken hatch from a duck's egg.

Before the mystery could be solved, Lise Meitner found herself forced to leave Germany as a "non-Aryan." She went first, via Holland, to Copenhagen, a broken woman, her most important lifework interrupted at its climactic stage. She could not get the mystery of the barium out of her mind. And the more she thought about it, the more convinced she became that this sub-microscopic bit of barium held the key to one of the greatest discoveries of all time. On reaching Copenhagen she communicated at once with another fellow exile, Dr. O. R. Frisch, who had found a haven in the physics laboratory of Niels Bohr, pioneer explorer of the atom's structure. With Dr. Frisch she discussed her daring hypothesis as to the origin of the barium, too revolutionary to be accepted by her conservative German colleagues. Meantime, on January 6, 1939, Drs. Hahn and Strassmann reported in a German scientific publication the strange phenomenon they had observed, stating that while they could not doubt the presence of the radioactive barium, they could not at the time offer any explanation of its origin.

To Dr. Meitner there could be only one possible explanation, and Dr. Frisch was quick to realize the enormous implications of that hypothesis. As so often happens, the explanation was very simple. Barium has an atomic weight nearly half that of uranium. Ergo, the barium must have resulted from the neutron's splitting the uranium atom into two nearly equal parts. It seemed impossible, inconceivable, contrary to all accepted concepts of the nature of the forces that held the atom together. These forces were known to be so vast that no power at the disposal of man was deemed great enough to overcome them, any more than one could conceive of a power to hold back the tides or to move the earth itself.

Could it be that the uranium atom was an exception, that it, the last of the elements, stood on the edge of the cosmos, as it were, so that, like a massive rock precariously balanced on the rim of a precipice, it could be pushed off with very little force, splitting in twain as it struck bottom? The presence of the barium seemed

33

to indicate that this was so. And if it was, they knew, the splitting should be accompanied by the release of tremendous amounts of energy. They also knew that this energy should impart itself, in the form of kinetic energy (energy of motion), to the uranium fragments, so that they would come flying out with tremendous speeds.

This suggested other experiments that would provide positive proof, or disproof, of their hypothesis. Through these experiments the exact amounts of the energy liberated could be measured, and these amounts, if high enough, would tell for certain whether the uranium atom had been split.

When Dr. Meitner arrived in Copenhagen, Dr. Bohr, who four years later was to help in the production of the atomic bomb, was preparing to leave for the United States, intending to spend several months at the Institute for Advanced Study, in Princeton, New Jersey. He was particularly anxious to discuss some abstract problems with Einstein, who, since his exile from Nazi Germany, had been a member of the faculty of the institute. But the news brought by Dr. Meitner, and the conferences during which she and Dr. Frisch had outlined to him their guess about the splitting of the uranium atom by a neutron, a process they had christened uranium "fission," had provided Dr. Bohr with problems much more concrete to discuss with the man who had been first to fathom the depths of the ocean of energy within the atom.

When he arrived in the United States on January 16, 1939, he found a cable from Drs. Meitner and Frisch waiting for him. They had performed the experiments and had obtained conclusive proof of the correctness of their guess. The uranium atom had been split. The two fragments flew apart with the unheard-of energies of 100,000,000 volts each, liberating a total of 200,000,-

000 volts. In simple terms this means that a source of energy had been tapped three million times greater than that liberated in the burning of coal and twenty million times more powerful as an explosive than TNT.

Immediately on his arrival at Princeton Dr. Bohr communicated the news to his former student Dr. John A. Wheeler and to other physicists at the university. From them the news spread quietly by word of mouth to neighboring laboratories. Without anyone realizing it at the time, the work on the atomic bomb got under way.

By a historic coincidence, Dr. Fermi, fleeing Fascist Italy, arrived in the United States almost simultaneously with Dr. Bohr and had accepted a position in the physics laboratories of Columbia University. Since it was he who had initiated the chain of events that led eventually to the fission of uranium, it was natural that he should be among the first to be informed about it. He called a conference of the Columbia atom-smashers, headed by Dr. John R. Dunning, and informed them of the big news. Plans were laid for a series of experiments to obtain an independent check on the Meitner-Frisch results. A tentative program for further exploration was outlined.

The Columbia experiments were designed to reveal the heavy electrical (ionization) pulses that would be expected from the flying fragments of the split uranium atoms. These pulses register the energy of the flying particles on an instrument known as the oscilloscope, which may be described as a species of atomic thermometer. The energy registers itself through lines in the oscilloscopes, in a manner similar to the rise of the mercury column in the thermometer with the rise of temperature.

Late on Wednesday night, January 25, the experiments at Columbia were concluded after a hectic twenty-

35

four hours in the vaultlike laboratory resembling a medieval alchemist's chamber. A tired group of scientists stood anxiously in front of the oscilloscope. At a signal someone pushed a button. Up jumped the line in the atomic thermometer to the staggering height registering 200,000,000 volts.

Before the experiments were concluded Dr. Fermi had left New York to attend a conference on theoretical physics, which opened in Washington, D. C., January 26, under the auspices of George Washington University and the Carnegie Institution of Washington. He sat next to Dr. Bohr when the latter rose to tell the assembly the news of the smashing of the uranium atom. And it did not take long for the significance of what Dr. Bohr was reporting in low, measured tones to be realized by the group of young atom-smashers at the conference. One by one they were seen leaving the lecture hall. The long-distance lines to research laboratories in various parts of the country became exceedingly busy. It was almost as though the young nuclear physicists, most of whom later played important roles on the Atomic Bomb Project, had a premonition of the need for haste. There was no time to lose. Without their being aware of it, the race was on.

In the famous Radiation Laboratory of the University of California, birthplace of the atom-smashing cyclotron, young Dr. Philip H. Abelson had also been working on the mystery of the strange brood of elements given birth by uranium bombarded with neutrons. He had devised an ingenious X-ray "microscope" with which he was hoping to identify these elements by telltale lines specific for each element. Like the Hahn-Strassmann-Meitner team in Germany, he was amazed to find X-ray spectrum lines corresponding to elements with only about half the atomic weight of uranium. Bewildered, he confided his difficulties to a colleague, young Dr. Luiz W. Alvarez, who was later to become, along with Dr. Abelson, one of the leading contributors to the Atomic Bomb Project.

On the morning after the conference at Washington, Dr. Alvarez was in the midst of a haircut at the Stevens Union on the University of California campus when his eye fell on a newspaper account of the discovery of uranium fission. Out of the barber's chair dashed Professor Alvarez clutching the newspaper in his hand. His blond hair only half cut, he rushed up the hill to the Radiation Laboratory. The much startled Dr. Abelson quickly forgot the strange appearance of his colleague, when he heard what he had to tell.

The discovery that uranium could be split and made to yield energies millions of times greater than those released by ordinary chemical processes, great and revolutionary as that was, would nevertheless not have been of any practical importance were it not for another, equally vital fundamental discovery that came almost simultaneously with the discovery of fission. It made it possible to utilize the vast energy released, both as a source of tremendous power and as the most devastating explosive the world had ever known.

This was the discovery that when the uranium atom splits, a few of the neutrons in its nucleus are set free. Since uranium could be split only with neutrons, this opened the staggering possibility that once the first uranium atom was split, it would liberate other neutrons that would split other uranium atoms, which in turn would liberate more neutrons. Thus what is known as a chain reaction would be set off similar to the chemical chain reaction occurring in lighting an ordinary fire with a match.

DAWN OVER ZERO: THE STORY

The discovery of fission may be compared to the discovery by ancient man of how to produce a spark. The second discovery, that in the process of uranium fission a number of extra neutrons are emitted, may be compared to the prehistoric discovery that a spark can be used for the purpose of starting a fire that will keep going without the need of any further sparks.

It was this discovery, not that of fission itself, that made the atomic bomb possible and opened the way to the utilization of atomic energy on a practical scale, for it gave us for the first time a practically inexhaustible source of neutrons at the expenditure of hardly any energy at all. Just as lighting a match starts the chemical chain reaction of the wood or coal fire, in which the energy in the outer electronic shell of the atom is liberated, so the neutron serves as a cosmic match, as it were, for starting the chain reaction that produces a cosmic fire in which the energy locked up in the inner core of the atom is set free.

Prior to this discovery of the fountain of neutrons gushing from split uranium atoms, neutrons could be obtained only on a very small scale at the expenditure of relatively enormous amounts of energy. This was done by allowing either the alpha particles naturally emitted from radium at high speeds, or a stream of charged atomic particles accelerated by a giant cyclotron, to strike a beryllium target. By these methods only a few out of the billions of bullets fired would hit a bull's-eye in the beryllium atom and thus knock a few neutrons out of its nucleus. It was like firing a million bullets to bring down one duck.

This was why before the discovery of fission, with its liberation of a self-multiplying stream of neutrons, no physicist believed that atomic energy could ever be utilized on a practical scale. In fact, only a short time before the discovery of fission became known, Einstein assured me that it could never be done. "We are," he told me, "poor marksmen shooting at birds in the dark in a country where there are very few birds."

A few months later Einstein was urging President Roosevelt to give serious consideration to the possibilities of uranium as the most destructive weapon ever conceived by man. We were no longer "poor marksmen." In fact, we couldn't miss. For it was realized at once that to start the chain reaction it would not even be necessary to produce the initial neutron to serve as the cosmic match. There are always a few stray neutrons present all around as the result of violent collisions between atoms in the air and highly penetrating cosmic-ray particles that constantly enter the atmosphere from outer space, or particles emitted from radioactive substances floating about everywhere in minute amounts. Neutrons thus liberated by such collisions immediately enter the nucleus of the nearest atom. Such a free neutron would serve as the match for automatically starting the cosmic fire.

But, one may ask, if that is the case, why does not this phenomenon occur spontaneously in nature? In fact, why didn't the uranium in the earth's crust blow up long ago, even before man appeared on the earth? The answer is that the chain reaction can take place only under special conditions that do not exist in nature. One of these is that the uranium must be of an extremely high degree of purity, such as had never before been attained with any metal.

The possibility that a geyser of neutrons would come gushing out on the splitting of the uranium atom suggested itself at once to Dr. Leo Szilard, Dr. Fermi, and others as soon as the fission phenomenon was discovered. The nuclei of the elements in the middle of the periodic table, resulting from the splitting of the uranium atom of atomic weight 238 (92 protons and 146 neutrons), can hold only a certain number of neutrons in excess of their protons. Any extra neutrons beyond that maximum would cause the nucleus to become unstable, and in such cases nature begins taking steps to regain her balance. This she may do in two ways: Some of the extra neutrons may give up their electrons, thus increasing the number of protons to the point where the proper ratio between protons and neutrons in the particular nucleus is restored. Or she may take more drastic steps by evicting some of the intruding neutrons bodily from her nucleus. She may also restore her balance by a combination of these two methods.

In the case of such an unprecedented cosmic catastrophe as the splitting of the uranium atom, mere theoretical considerations suggested that some neutrons would be set free in the act, either at the very instant of fission or soon thereafter. Since the first fragment resulting from fission to be identified was barium, of atomic number 56, the other half would obviously be krypton, of atomic number 36. Now, the heaviest isotope of barium found in nature has an atomic mass of 138, while the heaviest natural krypton isotope has a mass of 86, making a total of 224, or a mass fourteen neutrons less than the total in the U..238 nucleus, and eleven less than in U.235.

The difference could be accounted for in two ways: either the uranium fragments consisted of new, highly unstable isotopes of barium and krypton, of atomic masses ranging up to 143 and 146 for the barium and 92 for the krypton, or they consisted of new isotopes of atomic masses totaling less than 238 or 235. In the first instance nature would be likely to restore her balance by bodily ejecting some of the excess neutrons soon after the split occurred. In the second instance it would mean that some neutrons were liberated at the time of fission. In either case fission would be accompanied by the liberation of neutrons.

At the Washington meeting in January 1939 Dr. Fermi discussed with Dr. Bohr this possibility of the liberation of neutrons in sufficient numbers to start a chain reaction. The first experimental proof that this was indeed the case came very shortly afterward. By that time laboratories all over the world were working on uranium fission. Among the first to announce the proof were Dr. Frédéric Joliot, son-in-law of Marie Curie, and his associates Drs. H. H. Halban and L. Kowarski, of Paris. Their experiments revealed that as many as three free neutrons are produced by each uranium atom split. Experiments providing similar results were carried out simultaneously in the United States by Drs. Fermi, Szilard, H. L. Anderson, W. H. Zinn, and Henry B. Hanstein, who obtained independent confirmation that more than one free neutron is produced by each uranium nucleus undergoing fission.

It was still not certain, however, that these free neutrons would necessarily act as the triggers to start a chain reaction. By that time many of the characteristics of the behavior of neutrons had been learned. It was known, for example, that they first emerge with speeds of thousands of miles per second. A large number of these highly penetrating neutrons would therefore escape into the open air without splitting any atoms. Furthermore, certain elements present in unrefined uranium were known to devour neutrons. Such elements would therefore consume the free neutrons necessary to keep the chain reaction going.

Yet these two drawbacks, it was realized, could be remedied by taking certain measures. Since the distance that even the fastest, and hence most energetic, neutrons can travel has a definite limit, all one would have to do to prevent the free neutrons from escaping would be to make a uranium block of a size greater than the distance the neutron can travel. To put it another way, since the production of neutrons increases with the volume of the uranium block, whereas the escape is but a surface effect, a size can be attained at which more neutrons will be born inside the block than will escape through the surface. Such a size, the dimensions of which were not known until later, is referred to as the "critical size," or "crit" for short.

To prevent the neutrons from being devoured by elements mixed with the uranium—that is, impurities—it would, of course, be necessary to use uranium of a very high degree of purity. It was realized from the beginning that this would be a most formidable task, since only a few parts of impurities per million would be enough to spoil a chain reaction. Purity of such a high order had not been attained with any metal up to that time.

Even if these obstacles were to be completely overcome, however, it was soon realized that a third, even more formidable obstacle might completely frustrate the realization of the dream of utilizing atomic energy on a grand scale. This came with the discovery, regarded at first as a supreme tragedy and later as a blessing in disguise, that uranium itself eats up neutrons of certain energy levels without being split. Would the cannibalistic uranium eat up enough of its offspring neutrons to prevent a self-perpetuating, self-sustaining cosmic fire? No one could tell in those early days of 1939, so fateful to the history of the world. It looked to some of the scientists as though nature had brought man to the very gates of the promised land of atomic energy only to slam them shut in his face just as he was about to enter. To

42

others, particularly to the eminent exiled scientists in our midst, who were already anxiously watching the shadow of the Nazi war machine above the horizon, the cannibalism of uranium held out the hope of at least a temporary reprieve for mankind.

For from the very beginning it became obvious to Dr. Fermi and other fellow exiles that if a self-perpetuating, self-sustaining chain reaction was possible, uranium could be used for producing the most devastating explosion ever attained on earth. With the Nazis feverishly preparing for war while the democracies were still living under the delusion that Munich had brought "peace for our time," it appeared to them almost inevitable that the Nazis would be the first to harness atomic energy to their military machine, since that would make certain the realization of their goal of world domination. If uranium ate its young in large enough numbers, the joke, for the time being at least, would be on the Nazis. But no one could tell for certain. There was still the possibility that there were certain limits to the uranium appetite and that the neutrons multiplied at a rate high enough to satisfy this appetite while still keeping the cosmic fire burning.

And so, eight months before the shooting war started, began the battle of the laboratories.

CHAPTER FOUR

ON February 17, 1939, a meeting of the American Physical Society was held at Columbia University. Anyone not a nuclear physicist who by chance might have wandered into Lecture Room 301 of the Pupin Physics Laboratory at Broadway and 119th Street that day would have found the proceedings very dull indeed. Very few even among the physicists present were more than vaguely aware of the enormous social implications of the words being spoken or the symbols being written in white chalk on the blackboard. Yet these words and symbols changed the course of history. Through them the atomic bomb, and atomic power for the benefit of man, became a reality.

The participants included a large number of the pioneer explorers of the nucleus of the atom who later played a major part in the development of the atomic bomb. Among them were Drs. Bohr, Fermi, I. I. Rabi, Wheeler, Dunning, and scores of others who subsequently became leaders at Oak Ridge, Tennessee; Hanford, Washington; Los Alamos, New Mexico, and the many other centers of the Atomic Bomb Project. No mention of an atomic bomb was made at that meeting, but a number of those present, as I learned later, were already thinking, and worrying, about it.

44

The phrases that kept recurring through the discussions like a refrain were "chain reaction," "fast neutrons," "slow neutrons," "intermediate neutrons." On the blackboard the recurring symbols "U.238" and "U.235," scribbled by Dr. Bohr, were interspersed among graphs and mathematical formulæ. They represented the basic fundamental secret of the atomic bomb, written so plainly that even a non-physicist like myself could read.

The meaning of the symbols is very simple. Uranium as found in nature consists of three types (isotopes), all inextricably mixed together. All three have ninety-two protons in their nucleus, but each has a different number of neutrons. By far the most abundant type is uranium of atomic weight 238, which has 146 neutrons in its nucleus; it constitutes 99.3 per cent of all the uranium in the world. The second most common form is uranium of atomic weight 235, the nucleus of which contains 143 neutrons. It represents only 0.7 per cent of the uranium supply. The third type, uranium of atomic weight 234, contains 142 neutrons in its nucleus and represents only 0.008 per cent of all the uranium in the earth's crust. They are designated by the symbols U.238, U.235, and U.234.

In the three weeks that had elapsed since the Washington conference Dr. Bohr, in collaboration with young Dr. Wheeler of Princeton, had developed a theory of the fission process. It was this theory that he was expounding for the first time at the Columbia meeting.

In order to explain some puzzling phenomena observed in the various laboratories where experiments on uranium fission were carried out in the last week of January 1939, Drs. Bohr and Wheeler had worked out a hypothesis that fitted the facts and provided guideposts for future investigations. It was only a prediction at the

45

time, since no means were available to check it by experiment. But a little more than a year later, in March 1940, the prediction was confirmed by experiments carried out at the University of Minnesota, Columbia, and the research laboratories of the General Electric Company.

Neutrons coming out of atomic nuclei with very high energies, which make them travel at speeds of thousands of miles per second, can be slowed down, through elastic collisions with atoms of light elements, to speeds as low as one mile a second. An elastic collision takes place when a moving body collides with another body of nearly equal weight, as happens when one billiard ball strikes another. In such a case the moving body imparts some of its energy to the object it collides with, so that it is slowed down. When a moving object strikes a much heavier object, as, for example, when a rubber ball is thrown against a rock, an inelastic collision takes place, the ball bouncing back with almost the same energy it had to start with.

To slow down neutrons, they are, therefore, made to collide with elements containing a large number of hydrogen atoms, which have an atomic mass nearly equal the mass of the neutron, or with other elements of low atomic mass. Such slowing-down elements for neutrons, known as "moderators," are water, two thirds of the atoms of which consist of hydrogen; "heavy water," in which the hydrogen has an atomic mass of two, with one proton and one neutron in its nucleus; paraffin, which contains a large number of hydrogen atoms; and such light elements as beryllium and carbon. To serve as a neutron moderator an element or compound must not absorb too many neutrons.

In the experiments on uranium it had been observed

that both slow neutrons and fast neutrons produced fission, whereas neutrons of intermediate speeds were rather inefficient in producing a split. On the basis of these observations Drs. Bohr and Wheeler arrived at the conclusion that the fast-neutron and slow-neutron processes were due to two different isotopes of uranium. The fast neutron, they theorized, produced fission in U.238, whereas the slow neutron produced the splitting of U.235. The inefficiency of the neutrons of intermediate energies in producing fission was explained on the grounds that neutrons in that range of energies were the only ones that could be properly digested by the "cannibal" in the uranium, which, they predicted, existed only in the U.238. In other words, the energy level in the U.238 nucleus resonated in tune with the energy level of the intermediate neutrons, so that the U.238 nucleus could swallow one of them without suffering an attack of indigestion severe enough to make it burst.

In such an event—namely, the capture of a neutron of intermediate speed by the U.238 atom without the production of a split—the nucleus of the U.238 is increased in weight, as it now contains 147 neutrons instead of 146. In other words, the U.238 atom is transformed into a new isotope of uranium, of atomic weight 239 (U.239).

It was further believed, on the basis of empirical observations, that the probability of such a neutron being captured by U.238 was much greater than the probability of U.238 being split by a fast neutron. This was because it was found that a large percentage of the high-speed neutrons, the only ones that could cause fission in U.238, lost energy by inelastic collisions with the heavy U.238 nuclei without entering them. This meant that a large proportion of the fast neutrons emitted in the fission process would become intermediate neutrons of the energy range that could be swallowed by the U.238 without producing fission.

The importance of this finding, from the immediate military point of view, could hardly be overestimated. For it revealed that the U.238 would eat up so many neutrons as a result of their inelastic collisions that not enough fast neutrons would be left to maintain a chain reaction. This ruled out completely the possibility of using U.238 in an atomic bomb. The cannibal in the uranium turned out in reality to be the instrument of a benevolent destiny, for U.238 was the only type of uranium readily available in large amounts for almost immediate use. It made certain that the Nazis would not have atomic bombs in time to begin their war on civilization, which, as everyone sensed at the time, was just round the corner.

But the threat of the Nazis developing an atomic bomb was only postponed, not eliminated. For it was soon realized that U.235 could be split not only by slow neutrons but also by fast neutrons. More significant still, the theory gave strong grounds for believing that enough free neutrons would be liberated in both cases to maintain a chain reaction with fast neutrons as well as with slow ones.

This meant that U.235, if a method could be found for separating it in large quantities from the 99.3 per cent of U.238, could serve both as material for an atomic bomb of enormous destructive power, by bringing about an uncontrolled chain reaction with fast neutrons; and as a substance for utilizing atomic energy as a fuel two million times more powerful than gasoline, through a controlled chain reaction with slow neutrons.

The greatest obstacle that stood in the way at the time was that no method for concentrating U.235 in large amounts was known and the problems for developing such a method were of such magnitude as to make it obvious that it would involve unprecedented expenditures of time and money. Considering what they stood to gain by it, it appeared certain that the Nazis would get busy at once on an all-out effort to develop such a method.

But what about the democracies? Could they be made to realize the danger? Would they, who were not even producing tanks and guns and airplanes in adequate amounts, stand ready to venture millions, possibly hundreds of millions, on a weapon based on mere theory, the correctness of which no one could prove? One might as well expect Congress to appropriate millions for a perpetual-motion device.

But Dr. Fermi, who had been in this country only a few weeks, just refused to "know better." Immediately after the Columbia meeting he approached his chief, Dean George B. Pegram of Columbia, with plans to bring the matter at once before the proper Army and Navy authorities. With the aid of introductions by Dean Pegram, Dr. Fermi set off shortly thereafter for Washington.

After the publication of the discovery of uranium fission, when scientific periodicals in this country, France, and England devoted much space to new developments in this field, there came a complete blackout on further work on uranium in Germany. This silence was in itself strong confirmation of what our scientists had suspected from the very first. But even stronger confirmation came soon after, through bits of information passed on by the underground and newly arrived exiles. When pieced together, these bits revealed that a large section of the Kaiser Wilhelm Institute in Berlin had been set aside for intensive research on uranium, and that some two hundred top-ranking German scientists had been ordered to devote all their energies to the problem, which had been given top priority. The Nazis were at work on an atomic bomb.

At that time, as was learned later, work on the uranium problem and its possible military applications was being pushed vigorously in England. But in this country progress from a military standpoint was at first painfully slow. As Professor Henry De Wolf Smyth points out: "At that time [1939] American-born nuclear physicists were so unaccustomed to the idea of using their science for military purposes that they hardly realized what needed to be done." Consequently, as Professor Smyth states, the early efforts both at restricting publication and at getting Government support were stimulated largely by a small group of foreign-born physicists centering on Dr. Szilard, a native of Hungary, and including Professor Eugene P. Wigner of Princeton, Professor Teller, Professor Victor F. Weisskopf of the University of Rochester, and Professor Fermi.

While it was impossible to carry out large-scale experiments because of the unavailability of sizable amounts of U.235, it was nevertheless realized that even with a submicroscopic sample it could be determined whether U.235 was fissionable by slow neutrons, or fast neutrons, or both. If this was found to be the case, it would serve as proof that the Bohr-Wheeler theory was correct, and that, in turn, would lend strong support to the correctness of other predictions based on the theory.

The job of obtaining samples of pure U.235 was undertaken by Dr. Alfred O. Nier of the University of Minnesota, and Drs. K. H. Kingdon and H. C. Pollock of the General Electric Company's research laboratories at Schenectady. They built improved models of an instrument known as a mass spectrometer (to be described later), and by March 1940 they had produced the first bits of pure U.235 that ever existed on earth. Dr. Nier managed to produce two samples "weighing" one billionth and two billionths of a gram, respectively. Drs. Kingdon and Pollock managed to produce one weighing one hundredth of a millionth of a gram. At their rate of production it would have taken thousands of years to concentrate one gram, but those infinitesimal amounts, the most precious bits of metal in the world, were enough for the purpose. In a sense they were the first atomic bombs.

The samples were rushed to Columbia University, where they were subjected to bombardment by slow neutrons produced by the cyclotron. Those first historic tests were carried out by Drs. E. T. Booth, Dunning, and A. V. Grosse. The first sample, produced by Dr. Nier, was tested on March 3, 1940; the second, obtained by Drs. Kingdon and Pollock, on March 20; a third, concentrated by Dr. Nier, was tested on April 3. These tests established definitely that only U.235 could be split by slow neutrons, and that U.238 could be split only by fast neutrons, exactly as Drs. Bohr and Wheeler had predicted. Other tests in other laboratories soon revealed that U.238 eats up too many neutrons that have lost energy through inelastic collisions with it (intermediate neutrons), and therefore would not sustain a chain reaction.

By June 1940, another fact of the utmost importance for later developments became generally known both here and abroad. It was found that U.235 could be split not only by slow neutrons but by fast neutrons as well. Since slow neutrons do not occur naturally and require large quantities of a light element to serve as a moderator, it would be impossible to employ them in a bomb, as such a bomb would have to be of enormous dimensions. Furthermore, the reaction would be too slow. On the other hand, fast neutrons, if there were enough of them to sustain a chain reaction, could create an explosion of unprecedented violence in a small amount of U.235.

If there were enough of them to sustain a chain reaction—there was the rub. Nobody knew for certain whether there were, and yet this was the very heart of the problem. To find out whether a chain reaction with fast neutrons would be self-sustaining, sizable quantities of concentrated U.235 would be necessary, and that would take millions of years to produce by the best methods then known, unless hundreds of millions of dollars were to be spent to build mammoth plants that might or might not work. It was a vicious circle: no fast-neutron chain reaction could be demonstrated without sizable amounts of U.235, but no such amounts could even be dreamed of unless it could be demonstrated with a reasonable degree of certainty that a self-sustaining chain reaction would take place.

But how about using the unseparated U.235 in a natural mixture of uranium? Since fast neutrons would split both U.238 and U.235, why not take just a big block of uranium as found in nature, remove the neutron-absorbing impurities, and let a stray neutron start a chain reaction?

Luckily for the world, this was not possible because of the existence of the "friendly cannibal" in the U.238. Tests revealed that the number of neutrons captured and devoured by him without splitting would be great enough to prevent any chain reaction.

How about slow neutrons? The cannibal does not touch slow neutrons, whereas the probability of U.235 being split by slow neutrons had been found to be

52

greater than the likelihood of its being split by fast neutrons. These two factors should lead to a vast increase in the number of neutrons available to split more atoms, and the greater the number of atoms split, the greater the number of neutrons born. And if the birth rate of the neutrons available for further fissions is higher than their death rate, then a self-perpetuating chain reaction should take place in the U.235 even without separating it from the U.238. In other words, with slow neutrons ordinary uranium, as found in nature, could be used for determining whether enough neutrons were born through fission to maintain a self-perpetuating chain reaction.

If that was found to be so, it would serve as an indication that a chain reaction in U.235 could be maintained also with fast neutrons. For in a natural unseparated mixture of U.238 and U.235 the cannibal in the U.238 would still swallow a great many of the neutrons when they passed through the intermediary speed range, in the course of their being slowed down to low speeds. On the other hand, in pure U.235, which has no pronounced cannibalistic traits, nearly all the neutrons would be available for further fission and the production of an uncontrolled chain reaction—namely, a nuclear explosion.

The idea of testing the possibilities of a chain reaction with slow neutrons in U.235 unseparated from natural uranium occurred independently to Dr. Szilard, Dr. Fermi, and their associates at Columbia, as well as to scientists in England, shortly after the discovery of uranium fission was announced. It offered enormous obstacles, but it was the only way in which the feasibility of an atomic bomb could be proved by experiment, and without such proof there would be no justification for the enormous expenditures that would be entailed. As it turned out later, the decision to go all out on the Atomic Bomb Project was made a year before such proof had been obtained; but by that time strong circumstantial evidence was already available, and in the face of the national emergency that was considered enough.

In the words of Mr. Henry L. Stimson, when he was Secretary of War: "The decision to embark on large-scale production at such an early stage was, of course, a gamble, but, as is so necessary in war, a calculated risk was taken and the risk paid off."

And so at Columbia University, behind a thick veil of self-imposed secrecy, Drs. Szilard and Fermi, working at first independently along different lines, but joining forces later in a team that included Drs. Anderson and Zinn, George Weil and B. Feld, began work on the design of a structure in which, they hoped, a chain reaction with slow neutrons could be made to operate in an unseparated natural mixture of U.235 and U.238.

One of the first obstacles to be overcome was to find a suitable moderator for slowing down the neutrons. To serve as a neutron-moderator a substance has to be of light atomic weight (to produce elastic collisions), it must not absorb too many neutrons, it must be a readily available substance, and it must not be too difficult to handle. Drs. Szilard and Fermi came to the conclusion that graphite, the soft carbon used in lead pencils, best met all the requirements.

As Professor Smyth points out, it had occurred to a number of physicists that it might be possible to mix uranium with a moderator in such a way that the high-speed neutrons produced by fission, after being ejected from the uranium and before re-encountering other uranium nuclei, would have their speeds reduced below the speeds at which capture by the cannibal in U.238 is highly probable. But while the general scheme of using

54

a moderator mixed with the uranium was pretty obvious, Drs. Szilard and Fermi worked out a specific manner of using such a moderator, which laid the foundation for the gigantic atomic power plants, or "piles," later erected at the Hanford Engineer Works near Pasco, Washington. It was their idea to build a gigantic lattice in which large lumps of natural uranium are embedded in a matrix of graphite as a moderator of the neutrons. This, with some modifications, is the basic design later utilized so successfully in the atomic piles producing atomic bomb material.

Such a pile consists of large blocks of the purest graphite ever made, piled up in a structure forming an enormous cube. Channels spaced at definite intervals in these graphite blocks, which give it the appearance of a giant honeycomb, are filled with lumps of uranium metal. Enormous volumes of water circulating through the channels carry away the tremendous quantities of heat in which the energy liberated by the split atoms of U.235 manifests itself.

In such a structure, if the proper dimensions are attained, the chain reaction starts in the following manner: Some stray neutrons from within or without the pile split some atoms of the U.235 in the mixture. The split atoms liberate from one to three neutrons each, some of which are swallowed by the U.238 while others pass through the graphite, which slows them down. These slow neutrons, in turn, split other U.235 atoms, which liberate more neutrons, which split more atoms.

The geometrical arrangement of the uranium-graphite lattice is such that for every hundred neutrons that go into splitting U.235 atoms a little more than a hundred fission-producing neutrons are emitted. The ratio of the number of fission-producing neutrons in the second generation to the number of fission-producing neutrons in the first generation is known as the multiplication factor, and is designated by the letter K.

If, for example, 100 neutrons that had caused fission in a hundred U.235 atoms produced a brood of new neutrons of which 105 were left to cause fission, a ratio of 105 to 100, then the K factor would have a value of 1.05. If this factor is constant, then the third generation of fission-producing neutrons will be 105 multiplied by 1.05, and so on ad infinitum. When the K factor is greater than one, the pile will be chain-reacting, as the birth rate will be greater than the death rate. On the other hand, if 100 fission-producing neutrons give birth to only 99, then the K factor will be 0.99—that is, less than one, not enough to maintain a chain reaction.

When the Columbia group started planning the design of the first experimental pile, only minute amounts of uranium in metallic form were in existence, and no satisfactory method for its large-scale production, particularly in the high degree of purity required, was known. This was true also of graphite, for while graphite was plentiful, the available product contained too many neutron-absorbing impurities to serve the purpose.

In spite of these seemingly insurmountable obstacles, the Columbia group managed to get together enough crude material to erect their first pile in July 1941. It was a graphite cube of about eight feet on edge, and contained about seven tons of uranium oxide (compound of uranium and oxygen) in iron containers distributed at equal intervals throughout the graphite. Similar structures of somewhat larger size were set up in September and October.

Since the first piles were too small, because of the lack of sufficient material, and the uranium and graphite contained many impurities, they were not expected to produce a chain reaction. Much fundamental information, however, was gained through them and utilized later in the building of bigger and better piles. To make up for the shortage of neutrons, and for making comparative studies of the number of neutrons captured by the uranium and the impurities, as well as of the new neutrons produced through fission, the Columbia group placed near the bottom of the uranium-graphite lattice an artificial neutron source, consisting of a combination of radium and beryllium. The neutrons in this combination are emitted from the nuclei of the beryllium when they are struck by the alpha particles that are constantly being ejected from the radium nuclei.

In this type of structure, known as an "exponential pile," the neutrons are counted at various points throughout the lattice when no uranium is present in the graphite matrix, and the results are then compared with the number of neutrons emitted at the same points after the uranium has been put in place. The absorption of neutrons by the cannibal in the U.238 would, of course, tend to decrease their numbers, whereas the liberation of neutrons in the splitting of the U.235 atoms would tend to increase them. The problem is to determine which of these two opposing processes predominates.

For more than a year preceding the building of the first exponential pile, physicists at Columbia and at Princeton had been developing highly ingenious techniques for detecting neutrons and for measuring the amounts of their absorption by graphite and uranium oxide. By these methods they were enabled to detect and count not only the total number of neutrons emitted by a given system, but also to screen them in such a way as to count the neutrons according to their energy levels. In other words, they could distinguish between neutrons of high, intermediate, and low speeds.

In these studies it was found, for example, that the fast neutrons emitted in the process of fission, traveling at speeds of thousands of miles per second, are slowed down to the speed of thermal neutrons, going at only one mile per second, after being made to pass through forty centimeters (sixteen inches) of graphite. Since neutrons at this speed are the most efficient for producing fission, this showed that the uranium-oxide containers should be placed in the graphite matrix sixteen inches apart. In other words, it provided a blueprint for the geometrical pattern of the lattice.

By these techniques it was also possible to obtain approximations of the total number of neutrons that would escape through the walls of a graphite block of given dimensions, how many would be absorbed by the graphite itself, and how many neutrons of intermediate energies would be captured by the U.238 cannibal. Since these absorptions vary with the speed of the neutrons, each element absorbing neutrons of only specific energy ranges, measurements also had to be made to determine the various energy levels of the neutrons absorbed in the uranium-graphite system.

To provide a large source of neutrons for these experiments, protons—namely, nuclei of hydrogen atoms—were accelerated by means of a cyclotron and made to impinge upon a beryllium target. The neutrons thus liberated from the beryllium were equivalent to the yield of a beryllium target bombarded by the alpha particles from 3,500 grams (nearly eight pounds) of radium. This is greater by far than the world's total supply of radium. At the pre-war price of $25,000 per gram, such a quantity would be worth $87,500,000.

Most significant of all, by these techniques the Columbia and Princeton physicists (the latter including Drs. Wigner and Wheeler) were able to determine the number of neutrons emitted for each slow neutron entering the U.235. It was found that there was a little cannibal even in the U.235, so that not every neutron that enters it causes fission. Nevertheless, the studies showed that the decrease was not great enough to make a chain reaction impossible. It largely depended on how big was the appetite of the cannibal in the U.238. The data obtained gave reason to hope that if he devoured not much more than half of the average number of neutrons disgorged by the U.235, the balance would be great enough to maintain a chain reaction.

The problem was outlined by Professor Fermi in a lecture before the American Institute of Electrical Engineers in New York on January 24, 1940. "In order that a chain reaction might occur," he said at that time, "it is obviously necessary not only to have more than one neutron produced for every neutron that is absorbed in the fission, but also to be able to utilize for producing new fissions a large fraction of the neutrons produced; otherwise the loss might be larger than the gain. Assuming that two neutrons are produced in every fission, it is evident that for the chain reaction to take place more than one half of the neutrons produced must be used in new fission processes." Actually, Dr. Fermi said, "experiment shows that probably the average number of neutrons emitted is somewhat larger, between two and three."

Interpretations of the experimental data obtained from the exponential pile, involving many corrections, calculations, and approximations, gave a discouraging outlook. With the impure materials at hand, these data showed, a pile of infinite dimensions—that is, one from which no neutrons leaked away through its sides—would have a neutron birth rate of only 87 per 100. That meant a multiplication factor of only 0.87, not enough to maintain a chain reaction.

It was universally agreed that an increase in the purity of the materials, improvements in the lattice arrangement, and other factors would almost certainly lead to an increase in the multiplication factor. But even if limitless amounts of pure metallic uranium and the purest of graphite were suddenly made available, no one at that time could state whether a multiplication factor greater than one would be achieved.

There were many other discouraging factors. A number of fires broke out during the experiments, endangering the lives of the experimenters and necessitating fresh starts. In October 1941 a sphere of seventeen kilograms of powdered metal blew up in Dr. Zinn's hands, and he was severely burned. He was forced to spend three months in a hospital.

But the experiments continued. The scientists began referring to the elusive multiplication factor greater than one as "the Great God K." If "the Great God K" existed, he had certainly managed to hide himself very successfully. Was he a reality or only a tantalizing myth? Only the atoms knew and so far they had refused to tell. But unless proof of his existence could be found, there could be no atomic bomb and the vision of atomic power would be but a delusion. "The sheer cussedness of nature!" Professor Fermi sighed.

CHAPTER FIVE

AN important event in 1941 intensified the search for the multiplication factor greater than one. A group of workers at the Radiation Laboratory of the University of California bombarded uranium 238 with neutrons of intermediate speeds and discovered that these neutrons transformed the U.238 into an entirely new element, not known to exist in nature, which they named plutonium.

How this remarkable achievement was accomplished is a story in itself to be told hereinafter, but one outstanding fact about plutonium has a vital bearing on what is being related here: tests on the new uranium off-spring gave definite proof of an earlier conjecture that plutonium has the same fissionable properties as U.235, so that it could be used as a substitute of equal, if not even greater, efficiency.

It is impossible to overestimate the significance of this discovery, made by a group of young physicists and chemists (most of them still in their early twenties), as it opened the way for the first time to fissionable material in large quantities. In the separation of one element from another, advantage is taken of the difference in chemical properties between the two elements, which makes possible the employment of chemical means for large-scale separation. Since U.238 and U.235 have the same chemical properties, they could therefore not be separated by chemical means, whereas methods taking advantage of the slight difference in their atomic weight would yield, by the methods then known, only insignificant amounts. Plutonium, on the other hand, was an entirely different element from uranium, hence possessing entirely different chemical properties, which made it possible to employ chemical methods for its separation from the U.238 parent in large quantities. In a word, it meant that the material for an atomic bomb could be made available in time for use in the war.

The first submicroscopic bits of plutonium were produced by neutrons knocked out from beryllium by means of a cyclotron. By this method only insignificant infinitesimal amounts could be produced. But the fact that a neutron entering U.238 converts it automatically in a series of steps into plutonium proved beyond the shadow of a doubt that that is exactly what happens when the cannibal in the U.238 swallows a neutron. This had been suspected all along, but now there was conclusive experimental proof that it was an absolute fact. What that meant was that, if you could manage to build a chain-reacting pile, it might be possible to arrange it so that one out of every two neutrons emitted in the fission process from the U.235 would go into splitting another U.235 atom and thus keep the chain reaction going, while the second neutron would be captured by the cannibal and convert the U.238 into plutonium, which would be better than the U.235 since it could be separated by chemical means in quantities large enough for use in atomic bombs.

Moreover, an even more far-reaching possibility suggested itself concerning the use of a controlled chain reaction for the development of atomic power. The natural supply of U.235, as already stated, is very limited, each ton of natural uranium containing only fourteen pounds (seven tenths of one per cent). But the discovery of plutonium promised to make up more than a hundredfold for the niggardliness of nature. For, again on the assumption that half of the neutrons emitted by the fission of the U.235 in the pile would go into the making of plutonium, this would mean that for every atom of U.235 split, an atom of plutonium would be created. In other words, after the fourteen pounds of the U.235 in each ton of natural uranium had been completely used up through fission, fourteen pounds of plutonium would have taken their place. You would eat your cake and have it too.

Since the experiments with plutonium at California indicated that, like U.235, it would also undergo fission with slow neutrons, this meant that after the U.235 in the pile was all used up, the plutonium would take its place in perpetuating the chain reaction exactly as before, so that when the fourteen pounds of plutonium had been split up, they would have been replaced by an equal amount of the substance. In this manner the chain reaction could be kept going in the pile as long as there was any uranium left. In other words, all the 1,986 pounds per ton of U.238 in the pile would be eventually converted into plutonium, thus increasing the original amount of fissionable material by 140 times. This, of course, would mean a corresponding increase in the amount of atomic energy extracted from the pile, provided the plutonium had not in the meantime been removed for atomic bombs.

All these possibilities were reported on July 11, 1941 by Professor Lawrence, in a memorandum to the Committee of the National Academy of Sciences, which was then studying the uranium problem. This report played a major role in expediting Government support of the

Atomic Bomb Project on an all-out basis, and therefore must rank as one of our great historic documents. Following are pertinent excerpts:

An extremely important new possibility has been opened for the exploitation of the chain reaction with unseparated isotopes of uranium.

Experiments in the Radiation Laboratory of the University of California have indicated (a) that element 94 [i.e., plutonium] is formed as a result of the capture of a neutron by uranium 238 followed by two successive emissions of electrons (beta transformations), and furthermore (b) that this trans-uranic element undergoes slow neutron fission and therefore presumably behaves like uranium 235.

If this is so, the following three outstanding important possibilities are opened:

1. Uranium 238 would be available for energy production, thus increasing about one hundredfold the total atomic energy obtainable from a given quantity of uranium.

2. Using element 94 one may envisage preparation of chain reaction units for power purposes weighing perhaps a hundred pounds instead of a hundred tons, as probably would be necessary for units using natural uranium.

3. If large amounts of element 94 were available it is likely that a chain reaction with fast neutrons could be produced. In such a reaction the energy would be released at an explosive rate which might be described as a "super bomb."

At about the same time there came news from England that French scientists working at the Cavendish Laboratory, Cambridge, had (as the Official British Report stated later) "produced strong evidence, by December, 1940, that, in a system composed of uranium oxide, or uranium metal, with 'heavy water' as the slowing-down medium (i.e., moderator), a divergent slow neutron fission chain reaction would be realized if the system were of sufficient size." At that time, the British report adds, "it seemed likely that, if uranium metal were used, this critical size would involve not more than a few tons of 'heavy water.'"

This news from Britain, coupled with the news from the University of California, galvanized our scientists into action. For it was realized at once that the Nazis, through their rape of Norway, had gained possession of the world's largest plant for the manufacture of heavy water, and it was certain that they were using it as a moderator for a uranium chain-reaction pile. And since it was now almost certain that such a pile would produce plutonium in large amounts, it became once again likely that the Nazis might after all be able to produce atomic bombs in time for use against England, and also against Russia, which they had invaded in the summer of 1941.

It looked as though the cannibal in uranium was not friendly after all. In fact, the latest developments revealed him to be no cannibal at all. He was at the same time both a blessing and a curse, a Dr. Jekyll and a Mr. Hyde. There was good reason to fear that Mr. Hyde was likely to gain dominance over Dr. Jekyll, for until November 1941, nearly three years after the discovery of fission, we had approved a total of only $300,000 on projects for uranium, a mere trifle compared with the magnitude and importance of the subject, and it therefore seemed likely that the Nazis had got a head start on us in a race in which their opponents were trotting while they were galloping.

At that time the results of another study by Professors Wigner and Smyth of Princeton gave further reason for anxiety. The fragments into which the U.235 splits are highly radioactive, and since they differ chemically from uranium, it was realized that they could be extracted and used as a "particularly vicious form of poison gas." In their report Drs. Wigner and Smyth stated that "the fission products produced in one day's run of a 100,000-kilowatt chain-reacting pile might be sufficient to make a large area uninhabitable."

As Dr. Smyth hastens to point out, neither he nor Dr. Wigner recommended the use of radioactive poisons, nor has such use been seriously proposed since then by the responsible authorities. But, he adds, "serious consideration was given to the possibility that the Germans might make surprise use of radioactive poisons, and accordingly defensive measures were planned."

With all these dark clouds gathering on the horizon, our top scientists called a council of war. It was December 6, 1941, the day before "the day that will live in infamy." President Conant, who officially represented Dr. Bush, announced two important decisions. One was that "the possibility of obtaining atomic bombs for use in the present war was great enough to justify an 'all out' effort." The second was that the project was of such a magnitude that it required an entirely different type of organization from the one in existence at that time.

And so it was that on December 6 the decisions were taken that led to the end of the war that began a few hours later on the morning of December 7.

On November 7, 1942 a small group of men began assembling a huge collection of lumps of uranium and bricks of graphite into a spherical structure designed to force the Great God K to reveal himself. With the bricks and lumps of uranium and graphite, purer and more plentiful than ever before, they were building a gigantic latticework in which, they hoped, a cosmic fire would be lighted by a cosmic ray from interstellar space, and be kept burning by an endless relay of neutrons that would be liberated from split atoms of uranium 235. It was to be, as they referred to it in their matter-of-fact way, the first self-sustaining chain-reaction pile ever made.

The scene of their labors was a gloomy squash court underneath the West Stands of Stagg Field on the University of Chicago campus. No one passing the staid, ivy-covered neo-Gothic building on Ellis Avenue, between Fifty-sixth and Fifty-seventh streets, could have had the slightest inkling of what was going on inside. In fact, so great was the secrecy in which the work was shrouded that not even the president and trustees of the university knew what a hazardous venture was being made on their premises. And it was just as well, for their unawareness no doubt spared them many a sleepless night.

Much had happened since that historic day before Pearl Harbor as a result of the decision to go all out on atomic energy for military purposes. The sneak attack the day after lent even greater urgency to the undertaking. One of the first steps was to set up three great research centers, at Columbia University, the University of Chicago, and the University of California, to be directed, respectively, by Professors Harold C. Urey, Arthur H. Compton, and Ernest O. Lawrence, all Nobel prize winners. Those at Columbia and California were to be devoted to research and development of large-scale methods for the separation of U.235. The one at Chicago, which was named the Metallurgical Project, was to develop methods for the production and separation of plutonium. This, of course, meant the development of self-sustaining chain-reacting piles.

The Columbia group, including Drs. Szilard, Fermi, Anderson, Zinn, and Weil, as well as the Princeton group, including Drs. Wheeler and Wigner, who had been working on the pile problems, and scores of top-ranking nuclear physicists from our university laboratories, were therefore transferred to Chicago early in 1942 and went to work at once on plans for building a pile. Since they were still hampered by the lack of pure uranium and graphite, they continued their investigations along the lines started at Columbia and Princeton, and

67

in this way gained much additional knowledge on how to ferret out the Great God K.

But the problem of pure uranium metal and pure graphite had to be solved at the earliest possible date. So, on learning that the Westinghouse company had been producing small amounts of metallic uranium for research purposes, Dr. Compton called Dr. Harvey C. Rentschler, Westinghouse director of research, on the telephone. "How soon can Westinghouse supply three tons of pure uranium?" Dr. Compton asked. Dr. Rentschler was aghast; the total output of pure uranium metal up to that time had been a few grams. But he was assured by Dr. Compton that a large amount was needed urgently for a vital, highly secret war project, so Dr. Rentschler and his assistant, Dr. John W. Marden, set up a makeshift laboratory for the production of "metal X." Within a few months they had increased production from eight ounces a day to more than five hundred pounds and cut the cost from a thousand dollars a pound to twenty-two dollars. The three tons Dr. Compton had asked for were delivered by November 1942.

Other companies began production, and by May 1942 deliveries of uranium oxide with less than one per cent impurities began coming in at the rate of fifteen tons a month. A new and simpler process for purifying uranium ore, developed at the National Bureau of Standards by Dr. James I. Hoffman, was put in operation by the Mallinckrodt Chemical Works of St. Louis under the direction of Dr. John R. Ruhoff, who, as Colonel Ruhoff, was later in charge of procurement of metal for the Manhattan Engineer District, as the Atomic Bomb Project was known. As a result an additional thirty tons of oxide a month became available by July 1942. The Harshaw Chemical Company in Cleveland and the du Pont plant at Penns Grove, New Jersey, prepared, by a new simpler

68

process, the raw materials for final purification by the Westinghouse company, which had been doing this work by a rather slow and costly method.

Similar steps were taken to obtain graphite of the highest possible purity. Following suggestions made by the National Bureau of Standards, the National Carbon Company and the Speer Carbon Company began producing, by the middle of 1942, highly purified graphite that absorbed twenty per cent fewer neutrons than the best standard commercial material previously available.

By July enough purified uranium oxide from Mallinckrodt had become available to build an improved exponential pile, the ninth in a series of what were known as intermediate piles. The pile was not the right kind for a chain reaction, but the results obtained caused elation among the workers. Earlier tests in May had already revealed that the purified materials increased the neutron multiplication factor K from 0.87 to 0.98. Now for the first time calculations based on the data showed that in a theoretical "infinitely large" pile, from which no neutrons leaked away from the sides, the K factor would be 1.007, a value greater than one.

Even before this experiment, Dr. Compton had predicted that a neutron multiplication factor "somewhere between 1.04 and 1.05 could be obtained in a pile of highly purified uranium oxide and graphite, provided that the air was removed from the pile to avoid neutron absorption by nitrogen."

In the fall of 1942 a new and much more satisfactory method for producing pure uranium, developed independently by Professor Frank H. Spedding and his associates at Iowa State College, Ames, Iowa, and by Clement J. Rodden at the National Bureau of Standards, was introduced, and by the end of November more than one ton of metal had been produced by this method at a plant set up at Ames. Lumps of this product, the purest so far made, became known as "Spedding's eggs."

By November 7 a total of 12,400 pounds of pure uranium metal had been collected at the West Stands squash court. In addition there were many more tons of uranium oxide, and tons of graphite, both of a higher purity than ever before. Calculations on critical size—that is, the size at which the number of free neutrons produced by fission is just equal to the total lost by nonfission capture and by escape through the surface—assured them that they at last had enough uranium and graphite of sufficient purity to make a chain-reacting pile possible.

They approached their task with mixed emotions. They were naturally eager to succeed, but as human beings realizing the implications of success in this particular adventure, they were hoping, Dr. Compton told me, that they would fail. Though all their calculations seemed to point to success, they could by no means be certain. The calculations involved many corrections, approximations, and interpretations, and hence there was the likelihood of error somewhere along the line. Some miscalculation, some wrong intepretation, might vitally affect the result.

Keeping in mind Dr. Compton's prediction that they would meet with success "provided that the air was removed from the pile to avoid neutron absorption by nitrogen," they began building their pile inside a huge square balloon, from which the air could be pumped out later.

Every other detail had been carefully attended to. They had figured out the dimensions that would be required to obtain the critical size—that is, the size at which enough neutrons would be liberated inside to make up for all possible losses. They had devised all sorts

70

of controls, for normal use in operating the pile as well as for emergencies if something unforeseen happened. The squash court was full of all sorts of sensitive devices for counting neutrons.

These neutron-counters were, in fact, the instruments that were to reveal the presence of the Great God K as soon as he arrived, if he ever did; for by counting the neutrons from one generation to the next they would be able to tell whether the generations of fission-producing neutrons kept multiplying themselves by a constant factor greater than one or whether their death rate was greater than their birth rate. They knew only too well that without some system of birth control for neutrons an uncontrolled chain reaction might develop in which the neutrons would multiply in geometric progression so rapidly as to cause disaster for all concerned. Not that they were likely to produce an explosion even approximating that of an atomic bomb, as that could not happen except with fast neutrons liberated in a critical mass of either pure U.235 or plutonium, under special prearranged conditions. But an uncontrolled chain reaction even with slow neutrons in a large mass of uranium would liberate great quantities of atomic energy in the form of heat, and this heat, if allowed to become great enough, might vaporize the uranium and graphite in the center of the pile, and the vapor produce such tremendous pressure that it would explode the pile and the West Stands as well into a fiery cloud of uranium-graphite dust.

And that would be only part of the story. The extremely hot metal vapor might cause a Chicago fire even more disastrous than the one started by Mrs. O'Leary's cow; for the tremendous radioactivity of the flaming vapor would prevent firefighters from getting anywhere near the flames. Not only that, but the radioactive poisons that would be scattered over a wide area by the explosions would make the Chicago University campus and a large part of Chicago's South Side uninhabitable for some time. But the builders of the pile were not taking any such risks. In fact, it would have been impossible even to attempt to build a pile were it not for the existence of effective birth-control methods for neutrons. Two elements in particular, boron and cadmium, are voracious eaters of neutrons. So, as the pile was built up layer by layer, strips of cadmium and rods of boron steel were inserted at regular intervals in such a way as to make certain, to the best of their knowledge, that the number of neutrons would never rise beyond a desired level.

Since up to then atomic energy was being liberated in large amounts only in the sun and the stars, the pile they were building, which was to light an atomic fire for the first time on earth, was, in a sense, a miniature model of the sun or a star.

As a cradle for the star about to be born they laid a timber framework resting on the squash-court floor. The structure was to be, properly enough, a sphere, as that was calculated to yield the best results. The uranium-metal and uranium-oxide lumps were to be spaced in a cubic lattice, embedded in graphite. The graphite was cut in bricks and built up in layers. At the corners of the square graphite bricks in each alternate layer they placed the uranium lumps. The lumps of the six tons of the pure metal were placed in the center of the structure. Surrounding it was a latticework of graphite bricks, at the corners of which were placed lumps of purified uranium oxide.

Ten slots passed completely through the pile. Three of these near the center were to hold boron-steel rods for purposes of safety and control. The others were to hold neutron-absorbing cadmium strips for additional safety and for experimentation. Actually, any one of the cadmium strips alone could dispose of enough unwanted neutrons to keep the expected chain reaction within bounds. All that would be necessary to bring the neutron birth rate down to a desired level, at which it could not get out of hand, would be to push the cadmium strip to a measured distance within the pile, each centimeter of strip absorbing a definite number of neutrons. Conversely, to bring the birth rate up to the level at which the multiplication factor greater than one would appear, it would only be necessary to pull the strip out a definite measured distance. One of the three safety rods was to be operated automatically by two electric motors, which pushed the rod in when the intensity of the reaction increased above the desired level, and pulled it out when it was decreased below that level. Both within the pile and near it were placed instruments for measuring the intensity of neutrons at any given moment. A remote-control room was set up for use if it was found necessary to shut off the main room (where the pile was) because of lethal radiations.

From the very beginning the cadmium strips and boron-steel rods were placed in "retard" position to make certain that the desired multiplication factor did not appear by surprise. This later turned out to be very fortunate indeed, for it actually arrived much earlier than was expected.

The work proceeded from early morning until late at night for twenty-four days. With each layer the total number of the neutrons born in the first generation was found to be greater than that born at the previous layer, but the rate of increase was not great enough to maintain a chain reaction, as the multiplication factor K was in each case less than one. For each one hundred neutrons that produced fission, less than one hundred new fission-producing neutrons were being born.

Things were still going at about the same pace on December 1, when the eleventh layer was completed. The sphere was then nearly three-quarters complete and still there was no sign of a multiplication factor greater than one. Late that evening Dr. Fermi, who had been given the name Dr. Farmer for security reasons, had gone to bed. Dr. Zinn and the others stayed on working into the night. Somehow as they worked on, piling up the bricks of the twelfth layer, they thought they heard a marked change in the tempo of the clicks from the neutron-counters. With each brick the tempo seemed to increase. The neutrons were definitely coming out at a faster rate. Click, click, click. "We knew then," Dr. Zinn told me later, "that if we pulled out the control rods, the thing would pop. But we did not want to wake Dr. Fermi." It was unthinkable to open the show in his absence.

They were there early as usual the next morning, one of the coldest in Chicago. The squash court was badly heated, but the atomic bricklayers carried on in total oblivion of the cold and the gloom. Dr. Zinn was master of ceremonies that cold December 2. Present were Drs. Fermi, Szilard, Anderson, Weil, Compton, Wigner, Samuel K. Allison, N. Hilberry, Volney C. Wilson, John Marshall. There was one young woman in the group, Leona Woods, who later became Mrs. Marshall. Everyone present gradually became aware that one of the great moments in history was near. The neutrons were being born at a rate faster than had been anticipated for the twelfth layer of the structure. The calculations had apparently been on the conservative side.

By noon they were agreed that the goal might be near.

Another hour or two and the first self-sustaining chain-reacting pile in the history of man, generating atomic energy, might be a reality. And then Fermi, the imperturbable, said: "Let's go to lunch!" The room became empty and silent. The pile looked grotesque in its balloon, which had been found not to be necessary after all.

Meantime, three blocks away, a momentous conference had been in progress since early that morning in Room 209, Eckhert Hall, on the University of Chicago campus. Among the group were Dr. Crawford H. Greenewalt, chemical engineer, a member of the board of directors of the E. I. du Pont de Nemours and Company, Inc.; Roger Williams, assistant general manager of the du Pont explosives department; Warren K. Lewis, professor of chemical engineering at the Massachusetts Institute of Technology; and T. C. Gary, also of the du Pont staff. They had been selected for their engineering background as a reviewing committee to appraise the entire Chicago Metallurgical Project. None of them had the slightest inkling of the goings-on in the West Stands squash court.

In particular, they were discussing what was no doubt the strangest proposal ever made to the heads of a large industrial plant. The du Pont company had been asked by General Groves, who less than three months earlier had been placed at the head of the newly created Manhattan Engineer District, to undertake the construction and operation of large-scale plants, to cost hundreds of millions of dollars, for the production of plutonium and its chemical separation from its uranium parent. No such problem had ever before confronted a group of practical engineers and industrialists. They had been asked to construct a type of plant that nobody had ever built, to manufacture a product that had been made only in submicroscopic amounts, which nobody was sure could ever be made in quantity. Worse still, the only way to produce plutonium on a large scale was through a self-sustaining chain reaction, and yet there had been no definite experimental proof that such a chain reaction was possible. And even if they were to succeed in building these fantastic plants, involving tremendous engineering problems of a revolutionary nature, and managed to operate them successfully in the production of plutonium, it might still take years to work out a method for its concentration. How was one going to design plants for chemical procedures that still remained to be worked out?

And yet, as the discussion in Eckhert Hall proceeded that morning and continued in the afternoon, all these difficulties faded into insignificance in the face of one ominous possibility. We were at war. Our very existence was at stake. The Nazis had had a head start on us. All indications were that a chain reaction was definitely possible, and we could not afford to lose any more time. In a war for survival one must take calculated risks. The design and construction of operating plants must go on simultaneously with the laboratory experiments. That was a revolutionary concept never heard of before in industry. And there was the further handicap that because of the strict secrecy ordered by President Roosevelt, the industrialists could not be told what was going on underneath the West Stands of Stagg Field.

When Dr. Fermi and his team came back from luncheon and it appeared that the work was about to reach a climax, Dr. Compton obtained permission to invite one, and only one, of the group at Eckhert Hall to witness the proceedings. He called Dr. Greenewalt on the telephone. "Could you come over to the squash court below the West Stands of Stagg Field without delay?" Dr. Compton asked. "Don't ask any questions and tell no one where you are going." As Dr. Greenewalt arrived, the last pure uranium eggs were being placed in the corners of the graphite bricks. Dr. Compton made hurried explanations in whispers. The job was nearly done.

They were still not quite out of the woods, however. Nobody was sure just how sensitive the controls were. There might still be a last-minute catastrophe. So extra-special precautions were taken. Two young physicists in the group, Dr. Alvin C. Graves, of the University of Texas, and Harold V. Lichtenberger, of Millikan College, Decatur, Illinois, were selected to serve in what their colleagues referred to as a suicide brigade. They stood in silence on a high platform overlooking the pile, each holding a bucket full of a potent cadmium solution, ready to quench any fire that might start if the cadmium and boron bonds were broken. For two hours they stood there, waiting for a signal to go into action, hoping the while that the nerves and muscles of mere humans would respond quickly enough.

As the pile-builders were approaching what they suspected might be critical size, they proceeded more and more cautiously. A careful check was made on the automatic controls in the balcony. After the last egg had been deposited in its graphite nest, all the cadmium strips but one were pulled out. The last one was then pulled out slowly to the proper distance. The suicide brigade stood on the alert. Faster came the neutrons and more frequent were the clicks of the counters—eight hundred, nine hundred, a thousand, eleven hundred. Intently they stood around the recorder that gave the count of the number of neutrons per minute. In the eleventh layer the count of the first generation of neutrons had stopped at eight hundred. If it now rose to only a little more than sixteen hundred per minute they would know that a multiplication factor greater than one had been reached.

Click, click, click—twelve hundred, fourteen hundred,

sixteen hundred. And then there came a still small voice: sixteen hundred and one. Two, three, four, five. Six, seven, eight. Nine, ten. The atomic age had come in on tiptoe. The fission-producing neutrons were multiplying themselves by a constant factor of 1.0006; for each neutron that went into the splitting of one U.235 atom, more than one neutron was being born to carry on. A self-perpetuating chain reaction, and with it the dream of atomic power, had become a reality.

It was 3.30 in the afternoon of December 2, 1942. Along with the hour of 5.30 of the morning of July 16, 1945, this date and hour must go down in the annals of man as one of the two distinct birthdays of the Atomic Age—one marking the birth of atomic energy in a controlled reaction with slow neutrons; the other marking its birth in an uncontrolled chain reaction with fast neutrons.

As the critical size required to sustain a chain reaction had been found to be fully twenty-five per cent smaller than had been expected, the scientists added just one more layer, the thirteenth, for luck, and called it a day. In its final appearance this first man-made star was thus an incomplete sphere, flat at the top, a shape geometers call an oblate spheroid. As such it may be said to be a miniature model of the earth, except that it is flattened only at its North Pole.

Dr. Greenewalt lost no time rushing back to Room 209, Eckhert Hall, where the discussion of whether it would be wise for the du Pont company to undertake the construction of giant chain-reacting piles for the large-scale production of plutonium was still going on. "Gentlemen," Dr. Greenewalt said, "there is no need for further discussion." He had been sworn to absolute secrecy, so he could not tell anything about what he had seen. But, as Dr. Compton said, "though Greeney did not say anything, all you had to do was to look at him. Greeney's eyes popped," Dr. Compton added.

And as the reviewing committee decided then and there to recommend to the du Pont company to proceed with plans for designing, building, and operating mammoth piles for producing plutonium (which were completed two years later, under a dollar-a-year contract, at the Hanford Engineer Works, near Pasco, Washington, at a cost of nearly $400,000,000), Dr. Compton held a short long-distance conversation with Dr. Conant.

"The Italian navigator has arrived in the New World and found the continent much smaller than he thought it was," said Dr. Compton.

"I hope the natives received him kindly," said Dr. Conant.

PART TWO

Atomland-on-Mars

CHAPTER SIX

ON October 11, 1939, two weeks after the Nazis had crushed Poland, President Roosevelt took time out to listen to a man who was initiating him into the mysteries of the atom. The man who was explaining to the President the meaning of the fission of uranium and a self-perpetuating chain reaction was Russian-born, Columbia-educated Alexander Sachs, of New York City, a consulting economist and a director of the Lehman Corporation, who, because of his gloomy views and predictions on Nazi power and world destiny in the prewar years, had been dubbed the "economic Jeremiah." He had come to the President as the emissary of three exiled scientists, one of whom was Dr. Albert Einstein. They wanted the President to know that the Germans had started work on an atomic bomb, to be informed of the danger confronting us and the world and of the urgent need for starting such work in our own country. Through Sachs they offered their services to their adopted land.

Sachs's visit to the President had come as the result of discussions at Princeton, New Jersey, between Drs. Einstein, Szilard, and Wigner. In March 1939 Dr. Szilard had carried out experiments that proved conclusively that fast neutrons are liberated in the course of the splitting of uranium by slow neutrons. This, of course, opened the possibility of a chain reaction. Dr. Szilard had at once communicated his discovery, made independently at about the same time by Dr. Joliot in Paris, to Dr. Einstein, who in the meantime had already received disturbing news from Germany. They were soon joined in their discussions by Dr. Wigner. They decided there was no time to lose. Somehow they must manage to bring the matter to the attention of the President himself. It would be hopeless, they realized, to approach any lesser official. It is typical of the modesty of Dr. Einstein that he did not consider himself of sufficient importance to obtain an appointment at the White House.

It so happened that Dr. Szilard shortly thereafter met Sachs, who had on occasion served the President as an informal adviser. In addition to being an economist, Sachs had also displayed a keen interest in scientific developments. He was just the man Drs. Einstein, Szilard, and Wigner, and later Dr. Teller, had been looking for.

On that October day at the White House Sachs was reading to the President a letter Dr. Einstein had prepared for that occasion on August 2, 1939. In it he had written to the President as follows:

Some recent work by E. Fermi and L. Szilard, which has been communicated to me in manuscript, leads me to expect that the element uranium may be turned into a new and important source of energy in the immediate future. Certain aspects of the situation which has arisen seem to call for watchfulness and, if necessary, quick action on the part of the administration. I believe therefore that it is my duty to bring to your attention the following facts and recommendations.

Here Dr. Einstein described in simple terms the phenomena of uranium fission and the chain reaction, and pointed out that the main sources of uranium supply were outside the United States, that the United States has only very poor ores of uranium in moderate quantities, and that there was some good ore in Canada and conquered Czechoslovakia. As to that, Dr. Einstein reported to the President as follows:

I understand that Germany has actually stopped the sale of uranium from the Czechoslovakian mines which she has taken over. That she should have taken such early action might perhaps be understood on the ground that the son of the German Under Secretary of State, von Weizsaecker, is attached to the Kaiser Wilhelm Institute in Berlin, where some of the American work on uranium is now being repeated.

Then Dr. Einstein told the President the main reason for his concern:

In the course of the last four months it has been made probable through the work of Joliot in France, as well as Fermi and Szilard in America—that it may become possible to set up a nuclear chain reaction in a large mass of uranium, by which vast amounts of power and large quantities of new radium-like elements would be generated. Now it appears this could be achieved in the immediate future.

This new phenomenon would also lead to the construction of bombs, and it is conceivable, though much less certain—that extremely powerful bombs of a new type may thus be constructed. A single bomb of this type, carried by boat and exploded in a port, might very well destroy the whole port, together with some of the surrounding territory. However, such bombs might very well prove to be too heavy for transportation by air.

This is the first mention of the atomic bomb on record.

Dr. Einstein also enclosed the scientific report sent to him by Dr. Szilard, to which Sachs had attached a memorandum written by Dr. Szilard, explaining the contents and the meaning of the scientific paper in popular terms.

After listening attentively to what Sachs had to say, and carefully examining the Einstein letter, the President said:

"What you are after is to see that the Nazis don't blow us up."

"Precisely," Sachs replied.

President Roosevelt called in Brigadier General Edwin M. Watson, Secretary to the President.

"This requires action," he said.

This was the initial neutron that started a chain reaction that ended in a chain reaction of another sort over Hiroshima six years later.

At the order of the President, General Watson formed a committee to look into the matter. It was known as the Advisory Committee on Uranium and was headed by Dr. Lyman J. Briggs, director of the National Bureau of Standards. Other members were Lieutenant Colonel Keith F. Adamson of the Army Ordnance Corps, and Commander, later Admiral, Gilbert C. Hoover, of the Navy Bureau of Ordnance.

This committee held its first meeting ten days later. A number of scientists were invited to attend. Many of them expressed themselves as opposed to support of such a project by the Government. It was Sachs's task in those early days, he related afterward, to try to convince "these gentlemen of science and Government officials, including the Army and the Navy, to indulge . . . in a 'willing suspension of disbelief.' "

On November 1, 1939 a report was submitted to the President, which contained the following:

The energy released by the splitting of a mass of uranium atoms would develop a great amount of heat. If the chain reaction could be controlled so as to proceed gradually, it might conceivably be used as a continuous source of power in submarines, thus avoiding the use of large storage batteries for underwater power.

If the reaction turned out to be explosive in character it would provide a possible source of bombs with a destructiveness vastly greater than anything now known.

86

The military and naval applications . . . must at present be regarded only as possibilities because it has not yet been demonstrated that a chain reaction in a mass of uranium is possible. Nevertheless, in view of the fundamental importance of these uranium reactions and their potential military value, we believe that adequate support for a thorough investigation of the subject should be provided.

We believe that this investigation is worthy of direct financial support by the Government.

This was a step in advance over a previous adverse report, submitted by a technical adviser to one of the services following Dr. Fermi's first approach to Army and Navy representatives in March of that year. But, as Mr. Sachs commented, though the recommendations this time were more encouraging, "alas, we had no money."

In those days General Watson stood up against military and naval men who kept saying: "Well, this is still so remote; what is this thing? Let's wait and see." To which General Watson would reply: "But the boss wants it, boys."

Hardly any progress, however, was made in those early months. Mr. Sachs talked the matter over with Dr. Einstein, and on March 7, 1940, the scientist addressed a letter to him for presentation to President Roosevelt.

Since the outbreak of the war, [the Einstein letter read] interest in uranium has intensified in Germany. I have now learned that research there is being carried out in great secrecy and that it has been extended to another of the Kaiser Wilhelm Institutes, the Institute of Physics. The latter has been taken over by the Government, and a group of physicists, under the leadership of C. F. von Weizsaecker, who is now working there on uranium in collaboration with the Institute of Chemistry. The former director was sent away on a leave of absence apparently for the duration of the war."

He then went on:

I have discussed with Professor Wigner and Dr. Szilard the situation in the light of the information that is available. . . .

You will see that the line he [Dr. Szilard] has pursued is different and apparently more promising than the line pursued by M. Joliot in France. . . .

The first transfer of funds from the Army and Navy for the project that was later to cost two billion dollars was $6,000. This gives an indication of the pace at which the work was proceeding during 1940 and the greater part of 1941.

Meantime in Great Britain things were moving at a much faster pace. "The potentialities of the project were so great," Prime Minister Churchill stated, "that his Majesty's Government thought it right that research should be carried on in spite of the many competing claims on our scientific manpower." Accordingly, intensive work was started under Government auspices at the great British universities, principally Oxford, Cambridge, London (Imperial College), Liverpool, and Birmingham. Responsibility for co-ordinating the work and pressing it forward lay in the Ministry of Aircraft Production, advised by a committee of leading scientists presided over by Sir George Thomson. Later, on the recommendation of the Chiefs of Staff (whose advice had been asked by Mr. Churchill), urging "immediate action and maximum priority," a special division was set up within the Department of Scientific and Industrial Research, which, for purposes of secrecy, was called the Directorate of Tube Alloys.

Work on uranium was also being pushed in France during 1939 and through the spring of 1940 under the direction of Dr. Joliot. At the fall of France, in June 1940, Dr. Joliot sent two of his co-workers, Drs. Halban and Kowarski, to England. With them they brought 165 liters of heavy water—practically the whole world stock of this material—which the French Government had bought from the Norsk Hydro Company just before the invasion of Norway. They had smuggled it out right under the Nazi nose in one of the most dramatic episodes of the war. It delayed German progress in their uranium research by months, as subsequent events showed. Heavy water, in which the hydrogen has twice the atomic weight of the hydrogen in ordinary water, is an even more efficient moderator than graphite for slowing down neutrons.

Professor Joliot, who remained in France to play a major role in the underground, instructed Drs. Halban and Kowarski "to make every effort to get in England the necessary facilities to enable them to carry out, in co-operation with the British Government, and in the joint interest of the Allies, a crucial experiment which had been planned in Paris and for which the 'heavy water' had been acquired."

Work was also carried on in Denmark by Professor Bohr until the Nazis invaded his country in April 1940. He had a small supply of heavy water, which, to prevent its falling into the hands of the Nazis, he kept in a large beer bottle in the refrigerator. When, with the aid of the British, he escaped from Denmark in a small boat four years later, he took the bottle with him, only to discover on his arrival in Sweden that in his haste he had taken along just an ordinary bottle of good Danish beer. The heavy water in the beer bottle was later rescued by the Danish underground.

The first interchange of information on uranium among Britain, the United States, and Canada, under a general arrangement then in force for pooling scientific knowledge, took place in October 1940. On October 11, 1941 President Roosevelt sent a letter to Prime Minister Churchill suggesting that "any extended efforts on this important matter might usefully be co-ordinated or even jointly conducted." Accordingly, all British and American efforts were joined, and a number of eminent British scientists proceeded to the United States.

Such progress had been made by the British group that by the summer of 1941 Sir George Thomson's committee was able to report that, in the view of its members, "there was a reasonable chance that an atomic bomb could be produced before the end of the war." This news soon reached scientists in the United States. A first draft of the British scientists' report was made available to Dr. Bush and Dr. Conant in the summer of 1941. At the same time Dr. M. L. E. Oliphant, of radar fame, who was on a visit to this country, held several informal discussions with our scientists, and in particular with Dr. Lawrence. Oliphant told them of large-scale plans in Britain to push work on the subject to the limit. This visit of Dr. Oliphant, together with the British report and a report of a similar nature prepared by our own National Academy of Sciences, following discussions between Drs. Lawrence, Conant, and Compton, led to the famous decision on December 6, 1941, to go all out on atomic bomb investigations.

By the middle of 1942 the progress was such that it appeared feasible to initiate plans for the construction of production plants. In the meantime President Roosevelt had appointed a General Policy Group to advise him on the matter. This group consisted of Vice President Henry A. Wallace, Secretary of War Stimson, General George C. Marshall, Army Chief of Staff, Dr. Bush and Dr. Conant. By June 1942 this group recommended a great expansion and acceleration of the work. The construction phases of the work were assigned to the Corps of Engineers. On June 19, 1942 Colonel J. C. Marshall was selected by the Chief of Engineers to form a new Engineer District and carry on the work assigned to it. Two days later Colonel (now Brigadier General) Kenneth D.

Nichols, West Point Honor Graduate of the Class of 1929, was selected as Colonel Marshall's Deputy. On August 13, 1943, he succeeded Colonel Marshall as District Engineer, a post corresponding to that of president of a corporation. On August 16, 1942 the Atomic Bomb Project was officially launched under the camouflaged designation: Manhattan Engineer District. Its first headquarters were located in lower Manhattan.

By September 1942 it became evident that the project was of even greater magnitude and more difficult of accomplishment than had been anticipated. But there was no turning back. At all times the project had the whole-hearted backing of the President. On September 17, 1942, Secretary Stimson placed Major General (at that time Brigadier General) Groves, one of the ablest members of the Army Corps of Engineers, in complete charge of the Manhattan Engineer District. Five days later the President's General Policy Group appointed a committee to plan military policy relating to the project, such planning to cover production, strategic and tactical problems, and research and development. General Groves was named to sit with this committee and act as its executive officer.

Toward the end of 1942 the British proposed that an important section of the work should be carried on in Canada as a joint Anglo-Canadian enterprise. Accordingly a joint laboratory was established in Montreal at the beginning of 1943, under the administration of the National Research Council. Practically the whole of the Cambridge group, under Dr. Halban, was moved to Montreal.

During the spring of 1944 the Americans joined actively in that project, which now became a joint British-Canadian-American enterprise. Its scope was enlarged and later in 1944 a site was selected on the Ottawa River, near Petawawa, Ontario, for the construction of a pilot-scale pile, using heavy water supplied by the United States Government as the slowing-down medium. To protect the Canadian uranium supply for the United Nations, the Canadian Government took over the ownership of the rich uranium mines and extraction plant near Great Bear Lake. A large part of the uranium for the atomic bomb plants came from this Canadian source.

In August 1943 a combined American-British-Canadian policy committee had been formed to assume responsibility for the broad direction of the project as between countries. Interchange of information was provided for within certain limits. In the field of scientific research and development full interchange was maintained between those working in the same sections of the field. In matters of design, construction, and operation of large-scale plants information was exchanged only when it would serve to hasten the completion of weapons for use in the war. All these arrangements were subject to the approval of the Combined Policy Committee.

The funds for the project were drawn from a general non-earmarked "expediting account" provided by Congress. The funds in this account, which Congress kept replenishing to maintain it at a level of $600,000,000, were spent on certification by Under Secretary of War Robert P. Patterson, who signed and approved the Manhattan District contracts submitted to him by General Groves. Around September 1944, when the total of these contracts was approaching the two-billion-dollar mark, the Under Secretary began to get worried. So he asked Michael J. Madigan, a New York consulting engineer and an expert on construction, who was then serving as his Special Assistant, to look things over.

Mr. Madigan, a very practical engineer, went out and talked to various people and saw some of the vast plants that were growing up. He then came back and made his report.

"Judge," he said, "I have been all around and seen everything, and I am here to tell you that you have nothing to worry about at all—nothing to worry about. If this thing works, they won't investigate anything. And if it doesn't work"—he repeated slowly: "And if it doesn't work—they won't investigate anything else. Alongside of this," he added, "everything else that we have done will seem a sensible procedure."

CHAPTER SEVEN

WHEN, on the day before Pearl Harbor, the momentous decision was reached to go all out on the effort to develop an atomic bomb, the gun was fired marking the last and decisive lap in the greatest race of all time, with the outcome very much in doubt. Since there were strong grounds for believing that the Nazi scientists were far in the lead, it was realized that the grim battle of the laboratories had to be fought on two fronts, in the laboratory and in the field. On the one front the battle was to be waged with the greatest array of scientific and engineering talent, equipped with vast material resources; on the other, a specially trained corps would sabotage the Nazi atomic bomb laboratories and plants.

Consequently special intelligence groups, both civilian and military, were trained in the United States and Britain. Their mission was to find out where the Nazi atomic bomb plants and laboratories were located. This information was used in the selection of pin-point targets for British and American bombers, or of demolition jobs for saboteurs. These were either members of the the underground in the particular locality or specialty troops landed by glider or dropped by parachute.

When Norway was invaded in April 1940, British scientists at once called to the attention of the authorities the need to keep a watchful eye on the Norsk Hydro Hydrogen Electrolysis plant in Vemork, in the Norwegian province of Telemark. That plant was at the time the largest producer of heavy water, the production of which is a singularly slow business. Since heavy water, as I have said, is the most efficient moderator for neutrons, and therefore the most efficient substance for the construction of a chain-reacting atomic pile, and since even at that early date the possibility of producing plutonium for atomic bombs in such a pile had already suggested itself, it became evident that the possession of the only large heavy-water plant in the world would give the Nazis a tremendous advantage.

As early as September 1939, German scientists had publicly stated that the manufacture of heavy water might become vitally important to their war effort. In May 1940, after the fall of Norway, the British Ministry of Economic Warfare received the disturbing intelligence that Germany had ordered Norsk Hydro to increase heavy-water production to 3,000 pounds a year. In 1942 it was learned that Germany demanded a further increase to 10,000 pounds.

This demand called for immediate action, as by that time British scientists were practically certain that, given sufficient heavy water and uranium, a chain-reacting pile could be made to operate. Since the Nazis had already placed an embargo on the export of uranium from Czechoslovakia, it became absolutely certain that they were building atomic piles.

The matter was referred by the Ministry of Economic Warfare to Special Forces, the Allied organization entrusted at that time with the responsibility of co-ordinating resistance in the enemy-occupied countries, which, it was hoped, would have contacts in the area. It so happened that one of a party of Special Force

Norwegians who, on March 17, 1942, had captured a Norwegian coastal steamer (the S.S. *Galtesund*) and brought it from Norway to Aberdeen, had considerable knowledge of the neighborhood of Vemork and had been in touch with some of the Norsk Hydro engineers.

Einar, as he may be called, was given hurried training and precise instructions and was dropped back by parachute on Telemark on March 28. To the end he remained a permanent feature of the heavy-water operations, one of the great epics of the war. A small follow-up party was formed to be dropped on Telemark the following month, but weather conditions prevented the carrying out of the operation for some time, and diminishing hours of darkness put an end to all night flights for that season.

In July 1942, after further disturbing intelligence, the War Cabinet Offices approached Combined Operations with a request that Vemork should be attacked. They urged that the very highest priority be allotted to the project. Combined Operations then asked Special Forces to provide a small advance party to act as local guides and collectors of intelligence for a sabotage attack against the heavy-water plant—the attack to be carried out later by Combined Operations personnel, whom it was proposed to land by glider.

"From the outset it was realized," the offical British report points out, "that the operation was exceptionally dangerous. Of all countries, Norway is the least suitable for glider operations. Its landing-grounds are few; its mountains thickly clustered, precipitous and angry. The broken countryside throws up air-pockets and atmospheric currents. Weather conditions in the autumn of 1942 were vile."

To add to the difficulties, the Norsk plant is located

on top of a high cliff overlooking the beautiful valley of
the Moon River, and was inaccessible from the front,
which was heavily guarded by a Nazi garrison, and from
the sides. The only possible approach was from the rear.
This required landing on a high plateau, making a
precipitous descent down the valley, and then climbing
up the steep cliff. The landing, of course, had to be made
many miles away from the valley in an isolated section
in the snow-covered mountains.

Special Forces provided an advance party of two
officers and two non-commissioned officers of the Royal
Norwegian Army's British-trained Linge Company,
named after Captain Martin Linge, D.S.C., a Norwegian soldier killed in action after the Commando landing at Maaloy on December 27, 1941. The party's leader
was named Jens. The others were Claus Helberg, Kjell
Nielsen, a chemical engineer who had worked at Norsk,
a man whose name is given only as Arne, and Einar, who
joined the party later and became its wireless operator.

Two attempts to drop the group in September failed
because of heavy clouds. The party, operating under the
code name of Swallow, finally made a parachute landing
on a mountainside east of Fjarefit in the Songadal, with
equipment in containers and packages, at 11.30 p.m. on
the night of October 15, 1942.

It took them two days to collect the equipment and
put it in order. Half the food supply and equipment
not immediately needed was hidden at a base depot,
to which it was planned that Swallow should retreat
when the operation had been carried out. The weather
was fine during these days, with patches of snow scattered lightly over the mountainside. But on October 21
a tremendous snowstorm burst in great violence, and
within a matter of hours Swallow saw the arrival of full

winter and fair skiing weather. Swallow advanced to the operational area.

The report of Swallow's leader takes up the story:

October 21, 1942

Claus and I skied with full packs into Haugedal, where I knew there was a hut. We failed to find it before nightfall, and heard later that it had been moved. Heavy march back, in the dark and mist.

The other two tried in vain to make radio contact with London. We had no paraffin for our Primus stoves and therefore had to ignore mountain routes where there was no wood to be found; so I decided to advance through the Songadal, where there were birch woods, and huts in which we could spend the night.

October 22

We set out on our heavy march. I hoped that our food, with the strictest rationing, would be sufficient for 30 days. We had been told to make no outside contacts except in the gravest emergency.

At high altitudes and in bitter cold, no man can be expected to carry a load weighing more than 30 kilos [66 pounds]. Our equipment consisted of eight such loads. This meant that, in our party of four, each man must make three journeys every day over the same stretch.

The ground was bad and rugged, the snow heavy and deep. Men who left the ski-tracks sank up to their knees. It was mild weather, and clumps of snow stuck to the bottom of our skis. The little bit of ski-way that we had we wished to keep for the retreat. The lakes, marshes, and rivers were not properly covered with ice, and could only be walked on here and there. There was surface-water on the ice, and we had our feet soaked all the time.

So our day's marches were sorrowfully short. We often advanced only a few kilometers a day. On the very first day I broke a ski-pole. It was a month before I got a new one.

October 24

We reached a deserted farmhouse at Barunuten, where we found meat and flour. We ate our fill for the first time since our arrival. We also found a ski-toboggan.

98

October 30

We reached Reinar. Now we are getting near inhabited places. We were very tired. I had a throbbing boil on my left hand and had to have my arm in a sling. We had kept ourselves in good shape during the waiting period in England, but the hard toil on short rations had sapped our strength. A day's ration consisted of a quarter-slab of pemmican, one handful of groats, one handful of flour, four biscuits, a little butter, cheese, sugar, and chocolate.

Claus was sent back to the empty farmhouse at Barunuten to steal all the food he could carry. Arne and the leader went forward to reconnoiter the line of advance. The W/T operator stayed to make a further attempt to contact London. A rendezvous was arranged for November 3. The leader continues:

Claus traveled to Barunuten and back—a distance of 50 miles —under terrible going conditions. He proved the old saying: "A man who is a man goes on till he can do no more and then goes twice as far."

Arne and I did not do many kilometers. I fell through the ice while crossing a river. This was the second time. Next day we tried to cross another river, but found no ice and returned, tired out, to Reinar, where the wireless operator told us that, just at the moment when he had succeeded in making contact with London, his accumulator had run out. Our plans had to be altered. The fulfillment of our job depended on our being able to find a new accumulator.

November 6

We reached our operational base at Sandvatn, completely exhausted but glad to have arrived at our destination. The march had taken 15 days. Claus had procured an accumulator from the keeper of a local dam at Msvatn.

The first thing we had to do was to get into wireless contact with England. We felt that they must be anxious about us. Antenna masts of a good size were put up. But we failed again —this time because the W/T set was damp.

November 9

We made contact with England at last. After this the wireless service went well. We prepared for the reception of the gliders.

Officers at Special Force Headquarters, London, breathed a sigh of relief when Swallow came on the air —even though the intelligence received lent to their relief a slight foreboding. The Germans, who had a strong garrison in the area, had set wire barricades around the factory and alongside the penstock lines that carried water down the mountainside to the factory's dynamos.

The glider parties stood by. "Mock-up" models of the machinery to be attacked, based on Swallow's intelligence, were built at a training school in England. Selected air-borne troops were trained for the specific demolitions required. Swallow, working in constant difficulty at an altitude of four thousand feet in a temperature continually below zero, daily transmitted weather reports and further intelligence with accuracy and punctuality.

On November 19 two aircraft, each towing air-borne troops in a glider, took off from Scotland. One aircraft and both gliders crashed on the southwest coast of Norway about one hundred miles from the target.

Jens, the Swallow leader, continues:

November 20

London's radio message about the glider disaster was a hard blow. It was sad and bitter, especially as the weather in our part of the country improved during the following days. But we were happy to hear that another attempt would be made in the next moon period.

This second attempt was mounted and manned by Special Force personnel only. Six volunteers from the

Linge Company were selected to form the assault party and given intensive special training.

The difficulties of attack had been multiplied. German interrogation of the air-borne troop survivors had enabled them to guess our operational objective. The Rjukan garrison was again increased, the area combed for saboteurs, and many loyal and innocent Norwegians were arrested. The German Reichskommissar, Josef Terboven, and General von Falkenhorst inspected the Vemork defenses in person. Special Forces were fortunate in having the services of the late Major Leif Tronsted, formerly professor of industrial chemistry at Trondheim University. His knowledge of heavy water and of the Vemork plant was unique.

Swallow waited patiently, continued their watch, and sent their signals, working in snow and ice, short of food, and with failing power in their W/T set.

The leader says:

December 18

To make matters worse everybody except myself became sick with fever and pains in the stomach. We were short of food and were obliged to begin eating reindeer moss. The W/T operator found a Krag rifle and some cartridges. I went out every day after reindeer, but the weather was bad and I could find none. Our supply of dry wood came to an end.

December 19

The W/T operator went to Langsj to steal food from a hut. He came back the next day with fish preserved in earth.

December 23

The weather cleared and at last I shot a reindeer. We celebrated a happy Christmas.

The same patience had to be exercised, and even greater nervous strain suffered, by the party mobilized in England. Although their training had been completed

101

and they were ready to leave, the weather prevented their departure. On the night of January 23, 1943 they actually flew over Norway, but after crossing over Telemark for two hours, were forced to turn back, as mist obscured the dropping-point and the lights that Swallow had laid out ready for their reception.

On February 10, 1943 Swallow signaled the exact position of all sentries and guards at Vemork. At midnight on February 16 the six Norwegian soldiers from Special Forces, operating under the code name Gunnerside, dropped by parachute on the frozen surface of Lake Skryken, thirty miles northwest of Swallow. A radio message from London informed Swallow of Gunnerside's arrival. But contact had still to be made, and a journey of thirty miles in the Norwegian winter can take as long as three hundred miles in warmer, flatter lands.

The Gunnerside leader's report takes up the story:

February 16, 1943

At midnight precisely my party of six landed safely on Norwegian soil. The jump was made from 1,000 feet. One package (containing 4 rucksacks) landed and was dragged by a wind-filled parachute for some 2 kms. [1.2 miles] before coming to rest in an open ice-crack, from which it was salvaged. One sleeping-bag and two rucksacks were damaged. Otherwise all our gear landed safely.

February 17

Our equipment was unpacked. Items required for the advance were repacked, and the remainder hidden to form a depot. The necessary stakes were placed as landmarks in the snow and their bearings taken. We finished our work at 4 a.m., by which time driving snow had already hidden every trace of the landing and the digging. We slept at an uninhabited hunting-lodge.

By 5 p.m. on the same day all was prepared for the first stretch of our advance. There was strong wind-driven snow and a moon. Our packs weighed 30 kgs. [66 pounds], and our two

OF THE ATOMIC BOMB

toboggans 50 kgs. [110 pounds] each. After an hour's heavy going, the drifting snow became so thick that it was impossible to find our way. I gave the order for a return to the hunting-lodge, which we reached at 8 p.m. It was then very cold, with a full westerly snowstorm.

February 18

A snowstorm of great violence burst upon us. It was impossible to go out of doors. All hands felt ill owing to change of climate. Two had bad colds.

February 19

Clear skies; but still the same storm, still the same driving snow. We made an attempt to reach the depot to fetch more food, but had to give up for fear of losing our way. During the night the chimney-pot blew off the hunting-lodge.

February 20

Clear skies, less wind; but still the driving snow. We made another attempt to fetch food, but the snowstorm had so changed the landscape that even our stakes were hidden. After three hours the attempt was abandoned. We made a final try the same afternoon and at length found one container. The position of the depot was re-marked.

February 21

The snowstorm raged with renewed power. Visibility zero. All hands were filled with a great weariness and lassitude, and the two men who had been suffering from colds were now seriously ill.

February 22

Today the storm blew itself, finally, to a standstill. The weather turned fine, and I gave the order to prepare for departure at noon.

February 23

Nearing Kallung we were alarmed to see two bearded civilian skiers in apparently first-class physical condition. I ordered one of my men to put on his camouflage ski-smock and a civilian ski-cap. He set out to make contact with the strangers. If ques-

103

tioned, he would say he was a reindeer-keeper on his rounds. The rest of us went into cover.

For a little, there was silence among the Gunnerside party as its members waited and wondered what would be the outcome of the meeting. Each man's hand hung near his holster. Then suddenly, above the noise of the wind, sounded what Joachim, the Gunnerside leader, described as "three wild yells of pleasure." Gunnerside was in touch with Swallow.

Swallow and Gunnerside reviewed the situation and jointly evolved an operational order, of which the following are extracts:

Intelligence

Fifteen Germans in the hut-barracks between the machine-room and the electrolysis plant. Change of guard at 1800, 2000 hours [6.00 p.m., 8.00 p.m.], etc. Normally two Germans on the bridge. During an alarm: three patrols inside the factory area and floodlighting on the road between Vemork and Vaaer. Normally only two Norwegian guards inside the factory area at night, plus one at the main gates and one at the penstocks. All doors into the electrolysis factory locked except one that opens into the yard.

The Plan

From the advance position at the power-line cutting, the following will be brought up: arms, explosives, a little food. No camouflage suits to be worn over uniforms. Claus to lead the way down to the river and up to the railway track. Advance to the position of attack some 500 meters [546 yards] from the fence. The covering party, led by the second in command, to advance along the track, followed close behind by the demolition party, which the Gunnerside leader will lead himself. The position for attack will be occupied before midnight in order to be able to see when the relieved guards return to the barracks. According to information received from sketches and photographs, we have chosen the gate by a store-shed, some 10 meters [9 yards] lower than the railway gates, as being best suited for

104

the withdrawal and as providing best cover for the advance. The attack will start at 0030 hours [12.30 a.m.].

Covering Party

Duty: to cut an opening in the fence. To get into position so that any interference by German guards, in the event of an alarm, is totally suppressed. If all remains quiet, to stay in position until the explosion is heard or until other orders are received from the demolition-party leader. The commander of the covering party to use his own judgment if necessary. If the alarm is sounded during the advance into the factory grounds, the covering party to attack the guard immediately. When the explosion is heard, it may be assumed that the demolition party is already outside the factory grounds, and the order is to be given for withdrawal; the password is: "Piccadilly? Leicester Square!"

Demolition Party

Duty: to destroy the high-concentration plant in the cellar of the electrolysis factory. At the exact moment when the covering party either take up their position or go into action, the demolition party will advance to the cellar door. One man, armed with a tommy-gun, takes up a position covering the main entrance. Those carrying out the actual demolition are covered by one man with a tommy-gun and one man with a .45 pistol. An attempt will first be made to force the cellar door; failing that, the door to the ground floor. As a last resort, the cable tunnel is to be used. If fighting starts before the H.C. plant is reached, the covering party will, if necessary, take over the placing of the explosives. If anything should happen to the leader, or anything upset the plans, all are to act on their own initiative in order to carry out the operation. Any workmen or guards found will be treated in a determined manner, as the situation may demand. If possible, no reserve charges will be left behind in the factory.

It is forbidden for the members of either party to use torches or other lights during the advance or withdrawal. Arms are to be carried ready for use but are not to be loaded until necessary, so that no accidental shot raises the alarm.

If any man is about to be taken prisoner, he undertakes to end his own life.

105

The Gunnerside leader continues:

February 27

The weather was overcast, mild with much wind. We left our advance base, a hut in Fjösbudalen, about 8 p.m. We started on skis, but were later forced to continue on foot down to the Mösvatn road. Along the telephone line it was very difficult, steep country; and we sank in it up to our waists. At Vaaer Bridge we had to take cover, as two busses were coming up the road with the night shift from Rjukan. We followed the road to the power-line cutting. It was thawing hard now and the road was covered with ice.

Skis and sacks were hidden close to the power-line cutting, from which we began a steep and slippery descent to the river at 10 p.m. On the river, the ice was about to break up. There was only one practicable snow-bridge, with three inches of water over it.

From the river we clambered up sheer rock face for about 150 meters [164 yards] to the Vemork railway line. We advanced to within about 500 meters [546 yards] of the factory's railway gate. Carried on a strong westerly wind came the faint humming note of the factory's machinery. We had a fine view of the road and the factory itself.

February 28

Here we waited till 12.30 a.m. and watched the relief guard coming up from the bridge. We ate some food we had in our pockets, and once more I checked up to make sure that every man was certain about his part in the operation and understood his orders.

Cautiously we advanced to some store-sheds about 100 meters [109 yards] from the gates. Here one man was sent forward with a pair of armorer's shears to open the gates, with the rest of the covering party in support. The demolition party stood by to follow up immediately.

The factory gates, secured with a padlock and chain, were easily opened. Once inside, the covering party took up temporary positions while the demolition party opened a second gate 10 meters [11 yards] below the first with another pair of shears.

I stopped and listened. Everything was still quiet. The blackout of the factory was poor and there was a good light from the moon.

At a given sign the covering party advanced toward the German guard-hut. At the same moment the demolition party moved toward the door of the factory cellar, through which it was hoped to gain entry. The cellar door was locked. We were unable to force it, nor did we have any success with the door of the floor above. Through a window of the high-concentration plant, where our target lay, a man could be seen.

During our search for the cable tunnel, which was our only remaining method of entry, we became separated from one another. Finally I found the opening and, followed by only one of my men, crept in over a maze of tangled pipes and leads. Through an opening under the tunnel's ceiling we could see our target.

Every minute was now valuable. As there was no sign of the other two demolition-party members, we two decided to carry out the demolition alone. We entered a room adjacent to the target, found the door into the high-concentration plant open, went in, and took the guard completely by surprise. We locked the double doors between the heavy-water storage tanks and the adjacent room, so that we could work in peace.

My colleague kept watch over the guard, who seemed frightened but was otherwise quiet and obedient.

I began to place the charges. This went quickly and easily. The models on which we had practiced in England were exact duplicates of the real plant. I had placed half the charges in position when there was a crash of broken glass behind me. I looked up. Some one had smashed the window opening on to the back yard. A man's head stood framed in the broken glass. It was one of my two colleagues, who, having failed to find the cable tunnel, had decided to act on their own initiative. One climbed through the window, helped me place the remaining charges, and checked them twice while I coupled the fuses. We checked the entire charge once more, before ignition. There was still no sign of alarm from the yard.

We lit both fuses. I ordered the captive Norwegian guard to run for safety to the floor above. We left the room.

Twenty yards outside the cellar door, we heard the explosion. The sentry at the main entrance was recalled from his post. We passed through the gate and climbed up to the railway track.

107

For a moment I looked back down the line and listened. Except for the faint hum of machinery that we had heard when we arrived, everything in the factory was quiet.

It is calculated that 3,000 pounds of heavy water were destroyed, together with the most important parts of the high-concentration plant. Five of the Gunnerside party crossed the border into safety after a 250-mile journey on skis and in battle-dress, under conditions of almost unendurable hardship and in the vilest weather. They were flown back to England shortly afterward. The sixth of their number, Knut, remained behind in Norway for other work. The Swallow party also remained to report results, and then gradually dispersed, leaving only the original Einar, now an exceptionally efficient W/T operator, and Claus.

From them London learned that General von Falkenhorst, Germany's Supreme Military Commander in Norway, visited Vemork immediately after the disaster. He described the operation as "the best coup I have ever seen."

Across the Special Force report on the activities of Gunnerside and Swallow, Prime Minister Churchill wrote: "What is being done for these brave men in the way of decorations?" Eight British and nine Norwegian military decorations were awarded.

Von Falkenhorst reacted energetically. The German guards were removed and punished. Once again the Gestapo combed Rjukan and once again arrested many innocent Norwegians. Mountain troops patrolled the area, some of whom fired nervously at one another. German reconnaissance aircraft hovered in the neighborhood, and one crashed. Mountain huts were broken into and burnt.

Claus was the only one of the party who came into

contact with the enemy, and his adventure is worth mentioning.

On the high Hardangervidda Plateau he was suddenly confronted, on March 25, 1943, by three Germans, who appeared round a hill 100 meters [109 yards] ahead, and started firing. He turned and went off on his skis, but after two hours found that one of the enemy would inevitably outdistance him. The story is best told, in a shortened form, in his own words:

I therefore turned round, drew my pistol, and fired one shot from my Colt .32. I saw to my joy that the German only had a Luger, and I realized that the man who emptied his magazine first would lose, so I did not fire any more, but stood there as a target at 50 meters' [55 yards'] range. The German emptied his magazine at me, turned, and started back. I sent a bullet after him; he began to stagger and finally stopped, hanging over his ski-poles. I turned back to get clear away, as the other two might come at any time. Half an hour later it was completely dark. After another two hours I went over a cliff, falling 40 meters [44 yards], damaging my right shoulder and breaking my right arm.

The following day Claus encountered another large German patrol, but his plausible story deceived them and they detailed an escort to take him to a German doctor. The doctor attended to him and dispatched him in an ambulance to the Bardkeli Tourist Hostel, where he was given a room. But as night fell, Terboven, the Reichskommissar of Norway, and his staff arrived and demanded accommodation. Claus was left undisturbed, and Terboven occupied the next room to him. Claus had actually dropped his pistol in the snow before he encountered the second German patrol that morning. Next morning all the guests at the hostel, including Claus, were bundled into a bus and sent off to Grini Concentration Camp, as one of the women guests had refused to entertain Terboven during the night. Using a certain amount of guile and aided by the lady, Claus distracted the attention of the armed guard and managed to change his seat from the back of the bus to alongside the driver and the door. Toward dusk he seized his opportunity, flung open the door, and jumped out. Picking himself up, he staggered across a field toward a wood, followed by the explosion of two grenades thrown by the guard, and pistol-shots fired by the motorcycle orderly who had preceded the bus. He escaped, and after other adventures succeeded in returning to Great Britian.

The Final Clean-Up

The directors of Norsk Hydro tried to persuade the Germans to halve the manufacture of heavy water, but were overruled. In England the Combined Chiefs of Staff recommended a more powerful type of persuasion. Accordingly, on November 16, 1943, strong formations of the 8th U. S. Bomber Command attacked the Vemork power station and electrolysis plant. A further 120 pounds of heavy-water stock were lost. The directors of Norsk Hydro restated their plea, and this time the Germans, a shade abjectly, granted it. On November 31, 1943 Swallow (the constant Einar) reported that all heavy-water installations at Vemork were to be dismantled and sent to Germany. On February 7, 1944 he added that the transport of existing stocks to Germany would take place in about a week's time.

This information was passed to the War Cabinet Offices in London, who that same day issued top-priority instructions that everything possible should be done to destroy the stocks in transit. By evening, approval had been obtained from the Norwegian Defense Minister in London to attack the stocks despite danger of local reprisals on innocent Norwegians. Immediate information to this effect was sent to Swallow, and to

Knut, the one remaining member of Gunnerside, who was then fifty miles to the west. Knut was instructed to join up with Einar, and to ensure that the remaining stocks of heavy water did not reach Germany. At the same time a message was sent to another of the Special Forces parties in Vestfeld to proceed to Skien and prevent any special cargo from Rjukan being loaded at the port.

On February 10 Knut was given permission to carry out a plan he proposed for sinking the Lake Tinnsjö ferry-boat *Hydro,* on which the remaining heavy-water containers would be loaded for the second stage of their long journey to Hamburg. A jubilant reply from Swallow contained a complete list of heavy-water stocks ready for shipment.

The enemy was on his toes. Special S.S. troops were drafted into the Rjukan valley. Two aircraft patrolled the mountains each day, and new guards were stationed on the railway line from Vemork to the ferry quay; but, by some freak of folly, not a single German guard had been posted on the *Hydro* herself.

Knut, the demolition-party leader, says:

At 1 a.m. on the morning of Sunday, February 20, 1944, I myself with three colleagues left Rjukan in a car that had been procured for the purpose. I went on board the *Hydro* with two men, while the third stood by the car on shore.

Almost the entire ship's crew was gathered below, around a long table—playing poker, rather noisily. Only the engineer and the stoker were working. They were in the engine-room, so there was no question of going in there. We therefore went down to the passenger-cabin, but were discovered by a Norwegian guard. Thank God, he was a good Norwegian. We told him that we were on the run from the Gestapo, and he let us stay.

Leaving one in the cabin to cover us, the other and I wriggled through a hole in the floor and crept along the keel up to the bows. I laid my charges in the bilge, hoping that the hole in

111

the bows would lift the stern of the ferry and render it immediately unnavigable. I coupled the charges to two separate time-delay mechanisms tied to the stringers on each side. These time-delays I had had specially constructed out of alarm clocks. I reckoned that the charge was big enough to sink the ferry in about four or five minutes.

I set the time-delay for 10.45 a.m. the same morning. This was the time (as I discovered on a previous reconnaissance trip aboard the *Hydro*) that would bring the ship to the best place for sinking.

By 4 a.m. the job was finished, so we left. The car took us to Jondal, and we were in Oslo the same Sunday evening.

A copy of the Quisling newspaper *Fritt Folk* was in Einar's hands early on Monday morning. Banner headlines announced the mysterious sinking of the ferry-steamer *Hydro* at approximately 11 a.m. on February 20. An explosion had been heard. The ship's forepeak had filled with water. Propeller and rudder were lifted clear, and certain railway trucks had trundled forward the full length of the deck, to fall irretrievably into the deep waters of Lake Tinnsjö.

Swallow came on the air later with a report to close the story. This said that 3,600 gallons of heavy-water stock had been sunk with the ship. Later the long-stop party at Skien complained bitterly that they were waiting, had marked down the ship that was to take the special cargo by sea to Hamburg, had made their plans to destroy her, and had all their preparations ready, but no special cargo had come.

"So it was," the official report concludes, "that the manufacture of heavy water ceased in Norway; and so it was that all stocks available to German scientists from that source were lost."

This was only one episode out of many in the epic "battle of the laboratories." Others cannot as yet be

112

fully told, but the one related will serve as a striking example.

So effective did the joint British-American counter-intelligence become in the last year of the European war, and particularly after D-day, that the German scientists were forced to keep moving their laboratories from one place to another; but they might as well have worked in a goldfish bowl. When we finally entered Germany we were so well informed that we even knew the street and number of the laboratory in any given city. Upon approaching a town, an advance party of our Positive Intelligence Group, headed by Major Francis J. Smith, would frequently get through the lines and head for the proper address, much to the amazement of the German scientists working there. On such occasions they would confiscate records and equipment, take the scientists back through the lines, and wait until the town was entered to complete the job.

Major Horace K. Calvert, Oklahoma City lawyer, was head of operations in the European Theater of the Positive Intelligence Group, with headquarters in London. Around December 1944 his group turned over to the War Department complete proof that the Germans were far behind us in the race for atomic energy. We were then absolutely certain that they did not have an atomic bomb.

After V-E day our P.I. men, some of whom were physicists, interrogated the leading German scientists at length and obtained a complete picture of the German effort to create atomic energy. What they found was reported by one of them, Professor S. A. Goudsmit, of the University of Michigan, Dutch-born physicist, before the Senate Special Committee on Atomic Energy. Dr. Goudsmit was the scientific chief of the mission that was sent overseas to find out what German progress had been made on the atomic bomb. The progress made by German scientists toward the construction of an atomic bomb was "negligibly small," Dr. Goudsmit found. He summarized the state of affairs in German nuclear research as follows:

1. German scientists had abandoned hope of making a bomb for this war.

2. They concentrated their efforts on production of atomic energy rather than an explosive.

3. They had not yet succeeded in constructing a pile, or self-supporting chain reaction.

4. The total effort expended on the atomic-energy project was small, even though it had the highest priority.

5. German scientists had no knowledge of our work.

6. They believed that they were ahead of our developments in atomic energy.

In Professor Goudsmit's opinion, based on a careful study of German documents, there were six principal causes for "the complete German failure in this field":

1. German scientists lacked the vision that the Allied scientists possess.

2. The Nazi Party and the German military placed incompetent scientists in key military positions.

3. Lack of co-ordination caused competition instead of co-operation among the various groups.

4. German scientists put into this field scarcely more effort than they would have into a peacetime research project, because they felt certain of their superiority.

5. German pure science had no support from nor contact with the military.

6. Allied bombing interfered with German progress.

When President Truman revealed to the world that we had perfected an atomic bomb, many of the leading German scientists, including Dr. Hahn, and Dr. Werner ("Uncertainty Principle") Heisenberg, were in Allied custody. When they heard the news, they flatly refused to believe it. "Propaganda!" they scoffed.

114

When doubt was no longer possible, the effect on them was so devastating that at least two, Dr. Hahn and another, attempted suicide. Dr. Hahn gave as the reason for his act a keen sense of guilt, as the discoverer of uranium fission, for having unloosed this terrible weapon on the world. The other frankly admitted that he made his attempt out of chagrin and self-accusation for having failed the Vaterland.

When their first shock was over, Professor Heisenberg, who headed one of the main divisions of the German atomic-energy project, rose and delivered a lecture to his colleagues on how the Americans made the atomic bomb. Allied scientists present on that occasion smiled. The Herr Professor was 'way off the mark.

CHAPTER EIGHT

IT was not until the beginning of 1943 that work actually began on the construction of the giant plants for the mass production of U.235 and plutonium. As stated earlier, the amounts of these substances available at that time could barely be seen under the microscope. By the summer of 1945 they were being manufactured in amounts sufficient, in the words of President Truman, "to destroy Japan's power to make war."

Those few who, like myself, had the privilege of visiting these plants, scattered over vast areas throughout the land, found it hard to believe the evidence of their senses. Even leading scientists, intimately connected with the project from the beginning, still found themselves in a state of wonderment. This was revealed to me in a conversation with President Conant several months before Hiroshima. "They won't believe you," he said, "when the time comes that this can be told. It is more fantastic than Jules Verne." "They'll believe it if it works!" I replied.

During the course of my journey I discovered that in less than three years our scientists and engineers, backed by our great industries, had built an Atomland-on-Mars, a scientific Never-Never Land, where the accepted "impossibles" of yesterday had become actualities of staggering dimensions, in both space and time. If a Rip Van Winkle had gone to sleep at the turn of the century and awakened to behold modern airplanes, radio, television, and radar, he could not have been more surprised than I was when I first visited the mammoth plants in which U.235 is being pried loose from U.238, or the great atomic piles in which U.238 is being transmuted into plutonium.

In the Spring of 1940, as I have said, the highest yield of U.235 by the best apparatus then known was at the rate of one tenth of a millionth of a gram (0.1 microgram) per day. At that rate it would have taken 10,000,-000,000 (ten billion) days (27,000,000 years) to produce one kilogram. To concentrate a kilogram in one day, ten billion individual units of the apparatus would have been required. Since the amount of the material for one atomic bomb has been stated to be between one and a hundred kilograms, and since President Truman has revealed that in August 1945 we were "prepared to obliterate every productive enterprise the Japanese have above ground in any city," it is reasonable to assume that by the summer of 1945 we were producing U.235 in amounts measured by the kilogram. This is an increase in less than three years by a factor of many billions. The work of 27,000,000 years had been telescoped into a time scale measured in terms of minutes, hours, or days, as the case may be.

The same was true with the atomic piles producing plutonium. The original chain-reacting pile at Chicago liberated atomic energy, through the fission of U.235, at a maximum rate of 200 watts. Now, it is known that the fission of one kilogram of U.235 releases a total of 25,000,000 kilowatt-hours of energy, so that if one kilogram of U.235 were to be split per day, it would mean an energy release of 25,000,000 kilowatt-hours over a period of twenty-four hours, or an average steady power level of more than a 1,000,000 kilowatts. On the assumption that each atom of U.235, when split, provides one neutron for converting one atom of U.238 into plutonium, so that each kilogram of U.235 split would yield one kilogram of plutonium (which, of course, is not necessarily the case), then a production rate of one kilogram per day would call for the building of a pile that would operate at a steady level of a 1,000,000 kilowatts, or a power level 5,000,000 higher than the original Chicago pile.

When the construction of plutonium-producing piles was planned in 1942, even before the Chicago pile had been completed, it was estimated that to produce one kilogram of plutonium per day a chain-reacting pile would have to release energy (through the fission of U.235) at 500,000 to 1,500,000 kilowatts, the rate, of course, depending on the number of free neutrons available for the conversion of U.238 into plutonium. The estimated power level was thus from 2,500,000 to 7,500,-000 times higher than the optimum 200-watt rate of the Chicago pile. By way of comparison it may be pointed out that the ultimate capacity of the hydroelectric power plants at the Grand Coulee Dam is expected to be 2,000,000 kilowatts, so that, at the higher rate, a pile producing one kilogram of plutonium a day would yield nearly as much energy as all the power plants operated by the world's greatest dam.

Since it was estimated that a single atomic bomb would require from one to one hundred kilograms of plutonium, it would have taken the Chicago pile from 7,000 to 700,000 years to produce a single bomb on the basis of the 500,000-kilowatt rate, while at the 1,500,000 rate it would have taken from 20,000 to 2,000,000 years.

Evidently the Chicago pile, while it served its purpose

of demonstrating the possibility of a self-perpetuating chain reaction, was not the answer for the production of plutonium in quantity. It was further evident that in order to produce plutonium in the proper amounts, in time for use in the war, it would be required to work out the design for piles several million times more efficient than the Chicago pile, which, of course, meant piles of radically different design. It was realized that such piles would have to be gigantic in dimensions and would cost hundreds of millions. Moreover, they would have to be built as a calculated risk, for no one could guarantee that, once built, they would actually operate as expected.

The quantities of fissionable material estimated to be required for the job, which give us a clue to the ultimate goals aimed at by the top men of the project, are hinted at in the historic third report by the Committee of the National Academy of Sciences, submitted on November 6, 1941. "If the estimate is correct," the report stated, "that 500,000 tons of TNT bombs would be required to devastate Germany's military and industrial objectives, from one to ten tons of U.235 will be required to do the same job." The report goes on to state that "if all possible effort is spent on the program, one might, however, expect fission bombs to be available in significant quantity within three or four years."

From this it can be seen that those in charge of the program were aiming at a production rate high enough to provide from one to ten tons, or 1,000 to 10,000 kilograms, of U.235 in a reasonably short time, so that it could be used "to devastate Germany's military and industrial objectives." From the President's statement we also know that by August 1945 we had enough to obliterate Japan as a military power.

We can obtain a further estimate of the magnitude of this achievement by examining the time factors involved.

Construction of the first large plant for separating U.235 began on February 2, 1943, and the first units were placed in operation on January 27, 1944. Construction of another giant plant for the same purpose, using a different process, began on September 10, 1943, and the first units began operating on February 20, 1945. Work on the first plutonium-production pile was begun on June 7, 1943, and it was put in operation in September 1944. A second and a third pile were in full operation by the summer of 1945, producing plutonium on a scale described as "very large"—large enough to produce atomic bombs of one to one hundred kilograms.

In two and a half years' time we had thus advanced from a rate of production that would have taken 27,-000,000 years for a kilogram of U.235, and 7,000 to 20,-000 years for a kilogram of plutonium, to a rate at which enough was produced in the course of a few months to end the war in a matter of days, or, had we so chosen, minutes. As President Truman put it:

We have spent two billion dollars on the greatest scientific gamble in history—and won. But the greatest marvel is not the size of the enterprise, its secrecy, nor its cost, but the achievement of scientific brains in putting together infinitely complex pieces of knowledge held by many men in different fields of science into a workable plan.

And hardly less marvelous has been the capacity of industry to design, and of labor to operate, the machines and methods to do things never done before so that the brain child of many minds came forth in physical shape and performed as it was supposed to do.

Both science and industry worked under the direction of the United States Army, which achieved a unique success in managing so diverse a problem in the advancement of knowledge in an amazingly short time. It is doubtful if such another combination could be got together in the world. What has been done is the greatest achievement of organized science in history. It was done under high pressure and without failure.

The surprises that meet the visitor to the various plants are not confined to the plants as a whole, their enormous dimensions, their novelty in design, their Olympian grandeur, their unique processes, and their awesome products. Individual surprises relating to the multifarious components and apparatus in each of the plants await the visitor at every turn. He no sooner recovers from one than he is confronted by another equally if not more startling. And when he thinks he has reached the saturation point, he soon discovers that he has barely scratched the surface.

For example, he enters one of the great buildings in which U.235 is being concentrated by the electromagnetic method. He no sooner passes through the door than he finds himself confronted by a monumental structure that practically fills the entire space of the building. Merely the appearance of this inner structure is impressive enough, but suddenly he learns the incredible fact that practically the entire monumental mass, occupying many tens of thousands of cubic feet, constitutes one gigantic electromagnet. Nothing approaching a magnet of this size was even considered possible before the war.

As though that were not enough, the visitor soon learns that this is only one of many such magnets, scattered in various other similar buildings of this one plant, sprawling over an area covering five hundred acres. He then finds that these magnetic mastodons form but a part of a colossal isotope separation apparatus, descendant of a device known as a mass spectrometer, which, before the war, occupied a small space in a physics laboratory.

The visitor then enters the main building of another plant, several miles away, where U.235 is concentrated by the gaseous diffusion method. He hears a roar from behind the massive walls and is informed that it is the sound of the molecules of a gaseous uranium compound racing through a barrier that separates the U.235 from the U.238. The barrier, he learns, is an entirely new product that had never existed before. It contains myriads of holes, each no larger than two fifths of a millionth of an inch. Casually he is told that this barrier consists of nearly ten thousand miles of porous tubing, encased in more than a million cubic feet of equipment, practically none of which existed before the war.

And then he finds out that the entire system of more than a million cubic feet is operating in a vacuum.

While this is by far the greatest continuous vacuum on earth from the point of view of dimensions in space, the vast number of individual units of the electromagnetic plant, the incredulous visitor learns, operate in an "atmosphere" so rarified that it is the nearest to nothingness ever attained. To find anything approaching it, one must take a journey into interstellar space.

Naturally, to produce a vacuum of such dimensions requires powerful diffusion pumps in great numbers. Such high-vacuum diffusion pumps are comparative newcomers to industry, and in 1940 new types were developed that were considered revolutionary. Compared with those at the plant in question, these 1940 high-vacuum diffusion pumps are crude, antiquated models.

Not only are the pumps producing the vacuum vastly more powerful than any in operation in industry, but their number, compared with that in other industries, is astronomical.

Since the plants operate in a vacuum behind heavy walls, unprecedented systems of automatic controls had to be devised. Here one comes upon the ultimate in technological wonders, gadgets upon gadgets, each performing a special job and recording its findings on a special control panel. There are the gadgets for detecting the slightest leak from or into the vast system. Other gadgets print on a tape where all the various fractions of the gaseous uranium are, and tell the watchful operator exactly what is going on anywhere in the several million square feet of the plant at any given moment. Still others tell how the uranium isotopes are being separated at any one of the thousands of stages in the complex process. To examine the gaseous diffusion plant's "brains," the visitor would have to take a ten-mile walk to look at every control panel on just one floor.

All this may help to clarify some of the confusion that has been plaguing the public mind as to whether or not there is an atomic bomb "secret," and if so, whether the secret could be kept. The answer is that there are not one, but hundreds, possibly thousands, of secrets, each of which will require engineering know-how of a high order to solve.

The secrets begin right at the start in the production of pure uranium and graphite. Each of these may take a nation with less industrial know-how many years to work out. All the multifarious gadgets and processes mentioned above had behind their development the combined engineering skill and secret processes of all our great industries, passed down from generation to generation, with improvements all along the line, for more than a hundred and fifty years. These will not be easy to duplicate.

We produced fissionable material by three different major methods. The number of secrets may be reduced if a nation decides to concentrate on only one; but each single method involves scores of new processes, new technologies, and new devices, as well as great improvements in the employment and design of older methods and apparatus.

This does not mean, of course, that we can keep these

secrets indefinitely, nor that some simpler methods may not be developed in due time. Nor does the question of whether or not there is a secret have anything to do with the real issue of international control of atomic energy, for it is obvious to anyone that unless measures for such control are taken, we shall be sowing the seeds of a suicidal war with atomic bombs. The problem goes much deeper than the trivial question about a secret. For even if we could keep the secret for centuries, some form of international control would still be essential for the good of ourselves and of mankind.

CHAPTER NINE

THE two great plants for concentrating U.235, covering a total of 1,100 acres, are part of a subdivision of the Manhattan Engineer District known as the Clinton Engineer Works, located on a 59,000-acre Government reservation eighteen miles to the northwest of Knoxville, Tennessee. In addition, the Clinton Engineer Works designed and built a plant for concentrating U.235 by the thermal diffusion method, which takes advantage of a difference in the rate of diffusion of light and heavy atoms in the presence of a gradiant in temperature; an experimental plutonium pile that served as a pilot plant for the larger piles and for the study of the fission products of uranium; a number of research laboratories; and one of the world's largest power plants.

The three great atomic piles for producing plutonium, as well as three chemical plants at which the plutonium is separated from its uranium parent and other impurities, are known as the Hanford Engineer Works. They are located on a huge Government reservation, comprising more than 400,000 acres, at an isolated semi-desert site fifteen miles to the northwest of Pasco, Washington.

A third major site, at Los Alamos, New Mexico, twenty-five miles northwest of Santa Fe, served as the research and development center at which the products of Clinton and Hanford were shaped for their ultimate objective. Here, around a nucleus of a few buildings that had been used by the Los Alamos boys' school, the greatest laboratory in the world, with a staff composed of scores of the world's outstanding physicists, chemists, mathematicians, metallurgists, "weaponeers," and leaders in other related fields, was organized by Dr. Oppenheimer. At this laboratory, to which our major universities contributed their fundamental research apparatus, the experimental work, as well as the design and construction of operable atomic bombs, was carried out. This included fundamental theoretical studies on the nature of the nucleus and the behavior of neutrons, the final purification of U.235 and plutonium, and the fabrication of the auxiliary material that goes into the assembly of the bomb.

In addition to the three principal sites operated directly by the Manhattan Engineer District, scores of new plants and expansions of existing plants, from New York to California, were erected to effect the rapid manufacture of specialized equipment, the refining of uranium and graphite, and the development and production of essential new materials. Besides the three great centers at Columbia, Chicago, and California universities, research was also carried on, under contract with the District, at twenty-seven other universities, four Government bureaus, and three research foundations. The total number engaged in the work, including those employed by contractors with the project, was considerably above 300,000, of whom only a small number were aware of the nature and purpose of what they were doing.

Since for reasons of security and safety the plants had to be located at isolated, sparsely settled sections of the country, the plans had to include living accommodations for the large number of construction workers and oper-

OF THE ATOMIC BOMB

ating personnel. This led to the building, in a matter of months, of four hidden cities, each as secret in its way as Shangri-La. The largest of these, officially named Oak Ridge, but known as Dogpatch, or just the Patch, to its inhabitants, is located on the Clinton Works reservation. In less than two years it became the fifth largest city in Tennessee, with a total population of 79,000. The second largest was Hanford, on the banks of the Columbia River in the state of Washington. Built as a construction camp for the Hanford plants, it grew in the course of one year to a city of 60,000 inhabitants, the fourth largest in the state, and dwindled down to zero in another year, as the construction job was finished. Several miles down the river was built the city of Richland, inhabited by the operating personnel of the Hanford plants and their families, with a population of 17,000 in the summer of 1945.

A small Government-owned and operated community, with a population that reached 5,800, was built at Los Alamos. It included so many world-famous scientists that it no doubt had the highest average I.Q. of any city in the world.

Oak Ridge was the administrative center of the atomic project, as well as the residential section of the Clinton Engineer Works. In many respects it was unique in history. There have been other hidden cities, but never one of its size that grew so swiftly. What was probably most remarkable about it was the fact that the inhabitants themselves, with the exception of a few key men, knew nothing about the city's purpose or what its giant plants were producing. The work was so compartmentalized that each worker knew only his own job and had not the slightest inkling of how his part fitted into the whole.

Only certain top-ranking scientists, engineers, and

Army officers had inside knowledge of the project, but even among them there were limitations. The head of one plant, for example, was kept completely insulated from other plants where different processes were used. On my return from the bomb test in New Mexico, I was not permitted to tell even Colonel Nichols what I had seen.

Not only did the workers not know what they were producing in the mammoth plants, which consume tremendous amounts of electrical energy; the vast majority of them could not even be sure they were actually producing anything. Since there are only fourteen pounds of U.235 per ton of uranium metal, and of course much less proportionately per ton of uranium compound, they saw huge quantities of raw material coming into the plant, but hardly anything coming out. This created an atmosphere of unreality, in which giant plants operated day and night to produce nothing that anybody ever saw, for the products were shipped in small amounts by special couriers with the greatest secrecy.

The secrecy frequently led to tragicomic situations. A trusted courier was dispatched by automobile to deliver a small box of material, the nature of which he was not told, to a certain locality several hundred miles away. He was cautioned that at the first sign of any unusual behavior inside the box he was to abandon the automobile in a hurry and run as far away from it as his legs would carry him.

Our courier asked no questions and went his way, taking frequent glances at the strange box behind him. Things went well until he came to the middle of a long bridge. Suddenly, from directly behind him, came a terrific boom. Out of the car he dashed like one possessed, running faster than he had ever run in his life. Out of breath and exhausted, he stopped to examine

128

himself to make sure that he was still in one piece. Meantime a long line of traffic had gathered behind his driverless car and the air was filled with the loud tooting of impatient motorists.

Slowly he made his way back to his automobile and found to his amazement that it was still all there. Peering cautiously inside, he was even more amazed to find his precious box on the same spot as before. He was used to strange things, this courier, so he took his place at the wheel and was about to continue on his mission when once again he heard a loud boom directly behind him.

Once again he made a dash for his life, heedless of the angry horns that by this time were sounding from a line more than a mile long. Still exhausted from his previous mad dash, he nevertheless managed to put a considerable distance between himself and his mysterious box.

Eventually he made his way back, to find his car and his box in the same spot where he had left them. This time, however, he found an irate traffic officer waiting for him. Beyond showing the officer by his credentials that he was a Government employee, there was nothing he could tell him. It turned out that there had been blasting going on underneath the bridge.

The average worker at Oak Ridge and elsewhere, when asked by some newcomer what he was making, might reply: "I'm making a dollar thirty-five an hour." Many believed that the whole thing was actually one gigantic boondoggle. Some were convinced they were engaged in the manufacture of a "death ray." There was considerable banter, often approaching the ribald, about the nature of the product. The stock jest among anti-New Dealers was that they were making "front ends of horses to be shipped to Washington for assembly." There were a number who believed they were manufacturing a chemical to convert blacks into whites, the whole thing being a pet scheme of Mrs. Eleanor Roosevelt.

There is the story of the high-ranking Army officer who had been wined and dined regally by the Chamber of Commerce of a near-by community. After the customary after-dinner eulogies by the leading citizens, the officer, an engineer not much given to oratory, rose and made his acknowledgments to his hosts. This over with, he said: "And now, gentlemen, in token of my deep appreciation for your very kind hospitality, as a sign of the confidence and respect I have for you, I have asked and been granted permission to tell you what we are making in these plants which have meant so much to your community. I am now going to reveal to you the war's top secret, the greatest secret of all time." He paused and waited for the suspense to heighten. "We are making," he said, and paused again, "wheels for miscarriages."

Life in the secret cities was a study in contrasts. As R. L. Duffus stated in the *New York Times*, "the centuries jostle each other." Only a few years back, the people at Oak Ridge, and at near-by Happy Valley, most of whom come from stock that has lived long in these Tennessee hills, were existing on their worn-out land under conditions not very different from those of centuries gone by. "Now, by a stupendous leap," to quote Mr. Duffus, "they have been projected into the twenty-first century. On one side of a certain highway there are tall stacks to dissipate the radioactive fumes from atom-splitting. On the other side is a plain log cabin, chinked with clay and whitewashed—and lived in less than three years ago."

The story of Dogpatch would make an interesting study for the sociologist, the medical economist, the public health authority, the criminologist, and many

130

others. It has a medical insurance plan, on a voluntary basis, that pays for itself after a subsidy for the first six months. It has a high health standard and a low crime record, with hardly any crimes of violence. Its population, with the exception of Richland and Los Alamos, is the youngest in the country and has a very high birth rate, believed to be among the highest in the United States. At one time it had seventeen different religious bodies, all worshipping, at different times, at one little colonial-style church on top of a hill.

With the bulldozers, carpenters, plumbers, and electricians also came books, musical instruments, artists' paints and brushes, and all other paraphernalia of American culture, reflecting every section of the country and all strata of American life, for Dogpatch, as well as Richland and Los Alamos, were extremely cosmopolitan communities, their residents coming from virtually every state in the Union. In Los Alamos, the population also included a number of American Indians and Spanish Americans, descendants of the early Spanish settlers in New Mexico. Simultaneously with the construction of roads and streets, sewers and waterworks went the building of schools, theaters, a library, a hospital, a dental clinic, recreation centers, baseball diamonds, tennis courts, and other facilities. Cultural activities began almost as soon as the first residents moved into their homes.

Industrialists and labor leaders could profit by a careful study of the labor relations in the District. There were no strikes, no jurisdictional disputes, no sit-downs. Members of AFL and CIO unions worked together side by side; union men and non-union men performed their various tasks in harmony. By a special arrangement with the chiefs of the AFL and CIO and the heads of the unions all grievances were submitted to arbitration

131

through a scheme worked out by the Army authorities. The labor leaders further agreed to refrain from sending organizers to the sites.

While the Army was the final authority, the communities in Tennessee, Washington, and New Mexico had complete local autonomy to run their affairs. There were many playgrounds, and the shouting and laughter of happy youngsters could be heard everywhere. The homes were pleasant and comfortable, the atmosphere in many of them reminiscent of that in a college town. There was one strict rule: no mention was ever made of the work going on in the plants, and, as far as one could determine, the women did not have the slightest inkling of what their menfolk were doing. When Colonel Nichols invited me to his home for dinner, he reminded me not to mention anything I had seen, as Mrs. Nichols had no knowledge of the nature of the project.

Oak Ridge, Richland, and Los Alamos were communities of green lawns and flowers. Men and women, most of them from cities, puttered around in their gardens, planting flowers, mowing lawns, discussing seeds with their neighbors, showing great pride in their newly learned horticultural skills. It did not take long for city and tenement dwellers to develop a love for the soil and for things that grow out of it after one has planted them with one's own hands.

The student of human values may be interested in the following episode. There were more than five thousand trailers in Oak Ridge, probably the greatest trailer camp in the world. Great care was taken to make their occupants happy and comfortable, yet there was noticed a feeling of social isolation, as though they were living on the wrong side of the railroad tracks. It was soon discovered that their principal complaint was a sense of

132

loss of identity, which was remedied by providing the camp with street names and an individual number for each trailer. Until they had an address they had considered themselves gypsies. A street and number gave them a sense of belonging. It apparently is not enough to have a roof over one's head. A roof is not home until it has an address.

The problem of carrying the workers to and from plants scattered over an area of more than ninety square miles presented a serious transportation challenge. So one day Colonel Nichols presented himself at the Office of Defense Transportation and asked the official in charge for five hundred busses.

The official was aghast. "Five hundred busses!" he repeated. "Impossible. Preposterous. What could you need that many busses for?"

"We have a big war project," said Colonel Nichols.

"No project can be big enough to need five hundred busses," the official replied. But he soon got word from higher up to provide the busses as quickly as possible and not ask any questions.

As it turned out, the 500 busses filled only 66 per cent of the need. By the middle of 1944 there were 350 busses operating on the area, while an additional 500 carried non-resident workers to and from their homes. From July 1944 to June 1945 the on-area busses alone carried 22,252,479 passengers. During June 1945 they carried 2,401,070.

The Clinton Engineer Works is bounded on the east, south, and west by the tortuously winding Clinch River for a total distance of thirty-six miles. Within the reservation there are five main ridges, running east and west. The northernmost is Black Oak Ridge, from which the town took its name. Next in order come East Fork

Ridge, Pine Ridge, Chestnut Ridge, and Haw Ridge, all wooded with oak and several species of pine. The variety of vegetation in this region is said to be wider than anywhere else in the United States, the area constituting a meeting ground between Northern and Southern varieties of flora.

The reservation is not far from the Great Smoky Mountain area, which lies east and southeast of Knoxville. To the west are the Cumberland Mountains. The largest towns in the area, besides Knoxville, are Clinton, from which the works derives its name, Harriman, and Lenoir City. The project covers part of two counties, Anderson and Roane, the greater part being in Anderson. It lies in the heart of the TVA country and is situated about twenty miles from Norris Dam, which provided one of the principal reasons for the selection of the site, the others being accessibility to water, remoteness from the coast, and isolation.

The town of Oak Ridge is in the northeastern part of the reservation, about eight miles from Clinton. One production plant is situated between Pine and Chestnut ridges. Another large plant is at the extreme western part of the reservation, fifteen miles from Oak Ridge proper. The experimental pile is at the southwestern part of the area between Chestnut and Haw ridges. Another process plant is in the area of a huge steam plant.

The total amount of lumber used by the Clinton Engineer Works from the latter part of 1942 to May 1945 was in excess of 200,000,000 board feet, almost the output of the state of Minnesota for an entire year. Around 400,000 cubic yards of concrete were used for foundations and some of the structural frames in the plant areas, or one eighth the amount of concrete used in Boulder Dam. Around 55,000 carloads of material and equipment were shipped to the Clinton Works from

November 1942 through June 1945, and these were only a fraction of the whole.

"Two years ago," said Colonel Nichols in the early summer of 1945, "I didn't know what a billion dollars could buy."

At the time the Manhattan District took over, there were about 3,750 residents on the land that was taken into the reservation. They were scattered over the entire 59,000 acres, which included the hamlets of Roberts-ville, Wheat, Scarboro, Happy Valley, and a large number of small farms on a total of over 800 separate tracts of land. The area was among the first in Tennessee to be settled, and great pains were taken to resettle the up-rooted families. Many of them took jobs on the site.

Old-timers on the reservation recollected a long-forgotten old man, dead for about fifty years, who had lived in the vicinity and whom the natives had regarded as a bit "touched." There are some who still remember that old man telling all who would listen of the visions that had come to him of a great city rising on their land, and great smokestacks of huge plants belching smoke to the sky. The memory of that old man's long-forgotten prophecy helped to persuade many of the natives to part willingly with ancient homesteads.

In this great American saga many a drama was enacted on the scene, in Tennessee as well as in Washington, when families refused to give up their old homes, even though they had been offered sums that to them must have seemed fabulous. They had lived on the land for generations, and though it was very poor land, which gave them only a meager livelihood for their toil, it was the land of their fathers and they did not want to part with it at any price. Army officers in charge were loath to move them, but in many instances they had no choice.

"We had to move burning fires from their fireplaces,"

Colonel Franklin T. Matthias told me in reminiscing about the early construction days at the Hanford Works. "Those fires had been burning for a hundred and twenty years, and they had to be carried out bodily." The ancient fires from molecules had to make way for the greater fire from atoms.

CHAPTER TEN

THE end of 1942 was marked by four outstanding developments in the Atomic Bomb Project. One of these, of course, was the spectacular production of the first self-sustaining chain reaction, which led directly to the second—the authorization to proceed with the construction of the plutonium plants at Hanford. At the same time it was decided to experiment with several different methods and thus lessen the possibility of ending up in a blind alley. Accordingly, orders were issued to proceed with the construction in Tennessee of the electromagnetic and gaseous diffusion plants for concentrating U.235.

The electromagnetic method is based on the principle that electrically charged atoms, named ions, describe a curved path as they move through a magnetic field. Atoms of different mass and the same electric charge, when moving with the same speed through the magnetic field, follow different circles, and the path of the heavier atoms, because of their greater momentum, has a longer radius than the path of the lighter atoms. The atoms are most separated after traversing half of their respective circles, at which point they can be collected in specially designed containers.

The gaseous diffusion method is based on the principle

that at any given temperature the molecules of a lighter gas move faster than the molecules of a heavier gas.

The apparatus developed for the electromagnetic separation of U.235 is known as the calutron, a name representing a contraction of California University's cyclotron. It is a gigantic offspring of the prewar mass spectrometer, the laboratory apparatus used mainly for determining the relative abundance of the isotopes of the elements, as well as for detecting the existence of isotopes. But while basically the calutron is designed on the principle of the mass spectrometer, the two are about as far apart as a modern transport airliner is from the Wright brothers' first airplane.

The calutron consists of four principal parts: a source for the production and acceleration of uranium ions (that is, uranium atoms stripped of an electron and thus carrying a positive charge of electricity); a large magnet to make the ions follow a curved path of different radii; collectors in which the separated ions are deposited; and a tube, chamber, or tank, pumped down to low pressure, in which the ions travel their different semicircular paths from the source to the collector. The tank is placed between the pole faces of the magnet.

Solid or liquid compounds containing the atoms to be separated must first be vaporized. The ions are produced in the source by an electric arc running through the vapor. They are then accelerated by a high-voltage system and made to travel at constant speed along curved paths in the magnetic field. Upon arrival at the collectors the ions are neutralized; that is, they give up their electric charge, and solid material is deposited.

A high vacuum must be maintained in the tank in which the ions travel, to reduce the number of gas molecules present, as these would collide with the ions and deflect them from their path, resulting in contamination and the collection of less U.235.

Credit for this remarkable transmutation of a laboratory instrument into a giant industrial plant, which in the course of three years increased the output of U.235 billions of times, is mainly due to Professor Lawrence. The electromagnetic method had been ruled out on the basis of three principal limitations that were believed to be inseparable from the process itself and therefore impossible to overcome. These limitations, it was universally believed, would make it impossible to obtain U.235 in appreciable quantities. Attention was therefore focused on other methods.

Dr. Lawrence had at his disposal the largest magnets in the world, incorporated in his giant cyclotrons, and he is the sort of man to whom the word "impossible" constitutes a challenge. So in November 1941, without any financial assistance from any Government agency, he proceeded to rip his original cyclotron apart and put its 85-ton magnet to use in a giant mass spectrometer, alongside of which all existing apparatus of its kind were mere toys. Within three months he had produced an amount of U.235 thousands of times greater than had ever been concentrated before, at a ten times faster rate. This quantity was sufficient to be useful in determining the properties of the material and to demonstrate that the electromagnetic method of separation held possibilities of ultimate success.

During the course of this preliminary work the Research Corporation made a grant of $5,000 to the University of California Radiation Laboratory, directed by Dr. Lawrence. In December 1941 the National Defense Research Committee, headed by President Conant, offered a Government contract to underwrite this phase of the research, and the grant from Research Corporation was returned.

After the preparation of the first sample, experiments were pushed day and night to increase the output of the equipment. By March 1942, alterations had raised the production rate for short periods by a factor of 500.

By May 26, 1942, the great 184-inch magnet, largest in the world, was turned on for the first time on the concentration of U.235. Its completion as the world's largest cyclotron had been indefinitely postponed some months previously in favor of its conversion into a giant mass spectrometer, the greatest by far ever built. The Rockefeller Foundation made a grant of $60,000 for the conversion, as a contribution to the Radiation Laboratory's war research.

This giant showed, by midsummer of 1942, that the electromagnetic method was practical, and that a large enough electromagnetic plant could have a critical bearing on the war and inestimable implications for the future. By the fall of 1942, plans for a small pilot plant to be built at Berkeley, California, were approved. It soon became evident, however, that time would not permit this conventional intermediary development between laboratory and production plant. Plans for the pilot plant were therefore abandoned and all efforts reoriented toward the single purpose of building a large industrial plant and putting it in operation in the shortest possible time.

Since the plant was to require a tremendous amount of electric power, it was decided to locate it in the Tennessee Valley. Stone & Webster was selected to design and build it. General Electric, Westinghouse, and Allis-Chalmers were the major suppliers of equipment. The Tennessee Eastman Corporation was picked to operate the plant. These companies established offices at the

University of California Radiation Laboratory early in 1943. Their scientists and engineers worked in the closest conjunction with the laboratory's physicists, chemists, engineers, and shop technicians to translate data, procedures, techniques, and equipment into a practical functioning plant design. Tests of the mechanical and electrical equipment for the plant's installations were carried on at the Radiation Laboratory simultaneously with the construction of the plant buildings. The results of these tests suggested many modifications of equipment to give smoother plant operation and increased output.

Building the plant involved problems of construction and design never encountered before, since it is the first and only one of its kind in the world, and there was no time even to construct a small plant that could serve as a model. It has 270 buildings of a permanent nature. Its peak operating personnel totaled 24,000.

Since the electrified atoms to be separated must travel in a very high vacuum, high-speed vacuum pumps such as never existed before had to be created. After much research, Distillation Products Company developed pumps that produce and maintain extremely low atmospheric pressures. No vacuum pumps operating at such high speeds and such low pressures were in use at the time in any other process.

Great difficulties also had to be overcome in designing extremely delicate control equipment for high-voltage current. Rectifier units had to be designed capable of supplying a certain amperage at a very high voltage. These requirements are far above those encountered in radio broadcasting and similar high-voltage power applications.

In the process for separating the uranium atoms the requirements limit to approximately 0.04 per cent of the mean voltage the maximum permissible variation in the value of high voltage supplied to the apparatus. Such precise regulation of high amounts of power at high voltages, to a load that intermittently acts as a short circuit, had never before been attained.

Because of the great scarcity of copper, and because time was more precious than gold, 27,680,000 pounds of silver, worth $400,000,000, were borrowed from the Treasury Department for use as winding coils and bus-bars for the multitudinous magnets. The solid-silver winding coils have a total length of more than 900 miles. Silver is as good a conductor of electricity as copper and is not harmed by the passage of current. The silver will be returned to the Treasury when conditions warrant. Meantime this great plant for producing the material for the atomic bomb is, among other things, also a branch office of the Treasury.

All the research involving the electromagnetic method for concentrating U.235 was carried out under Government contract at the University of California under the direction of Professor Lawrence. At the peak of the research, in August 1943, Dr. Lawrence was assisted by a staff of 1,266, including 465 laboratory and research workers, and 365 employed in plant operation.

The gaseous diffusion plant for separating U.235 is shaped in the form of a *U* and covers an area of several million square feet. The method is based on the principle governing the diffusion of gases known as Graham's law, as elaborated on by Lord Rayleigh in 1896.

According to Graham's law, the rates of diffusion of different gases through a porous medium are, under similar conditions, inversely proportional to the square roots of the molecular weights of the gases. For example, if one gas, A, has a molecular weight of 9, and another gas, B, has a molecular weight of 16, the rate of diffusion of gas A through a porous medium, as compared with

142

the rate of diffusion of gas B, will be in the ratio of 4 volumes of gas A (the lighter gas) to 3 volumes of gas B.

When a mixture of gas A and gas B is allowed to diffuse through a suitable porous medium, under ideal conditions, the ratio of gas A to gas B, in the portion first passing through the medium, will thus be 1.33 times greater than the original ratio of A to B. By subjecting the portion first diffused to the same process, a gas mixture in which the ratio of A to B is increased by a second factor of 1.33 can be obtained. In fact, the process can be repeated at will, finally achieving any desired ratio of A to B.

In a practical plant, however, the separation factor in this particular example will not reach the ideal value of 1.33, but may go as high as 1.2. As an example of such a plant, let us assume that the ratio of gas A to gas B is 1 to 50, and we want to change it to 1,000 to 1. Assuming that we obtain an increase in ratio of 1.2 of A to B at each stage, we would require a plant in which the diffusion process is repeated sixty times.

When our scientists and engineers first considered the possibility of separating U.235 from U.238 by the gaseous diffusion method, they were confronted with a host of obstacles that at first seemed insurmountable. Applying our example to the case of uranium will illustrate the magnitude of the separation problem. Since uranium itself is not a gas, some gaseous compound of uranium had to be used. The only uranium compound at that time known that could be converted into a suitable stable gas was uranium hexafluoride, a combination of one atom of uranium and six atoms of fluorine, which would corrode practically anything with which it comes in contact. And not only is this gas highly reactive, but it is actually a solid at room temperature and atmospheric pressure. For these reasons a study of other gase-

143

ous compounds of uranium was urgently undertaken. As insurance against failure in this search for alternative gases, it was necessary to continue work on uranium hexafluoride, particularly on divising methods for producing and circulating this gas.

It was realized from the beginning that a plant for the concentration of U.235 by the gaseous diffusion method had to be of enormous dimensions, regardless of whether uranium hexafluoride or some other type of uranium gas was used. This can be illustrated by taking uranium hexafluoride as an example, though it would apply to other uranium gases as well.

The molecular weight of uranium 238 hexafluoride is 352, whereas the uranium-fluorine gas containing six atoms of fluorine and one atom of uranium 235 has a molecular weight of 349. Since, according to Graham's law, the rate of diffusion of the gas containing U.235, as compared with the gas containing U.238, would be inversely proportional to the square roots of their molecular weights—that is, in the ratio of the square root of 352 (18.76) to the square root of 349 (18.68)—the increase of the concentration of the U.235 hexafluoride would be by a factor of only 1.0043. Under actual operating conditions this value is even smaller.

This is, indeed, a very small enrichment factor. Hence, to bring it up to the desired level, it became necessary to design and construct a gigantic cascade in which the gas to be separated is made to pass through thousands of successive stages, each stage enriching the proportion of the U.235 gas over the preceding stage, the enriched mixture passing on to the next stage, where it is further enriched. No such plant for separation of gases had ever been designed or even conceived.

One of the principal problems that had to be solved before the plant could be built involved the development

144

of a suitable porous medium, or barrier, through which the uranium-gas mixture had to be diffused in a manner to allow a greater proportion of U.235 to pass through than of U.238.

It had been established that the pores of the barrier through which a gas mixture is diffused must be considerably smaller than the average distance a gas molecule travels before it collides with another gas molecule, a distance known as the "mean free path." At atmospheric pressure the mean free path of a molecule is of the order of a ten-thousandth of a millimeter, or a tenth of a micron. To ensure true diffusive flow of the gas, the diameter of the myriad holes in the barrier must be less than one tenth of the mean free path—that is, about one hundredth of a micron, or about four ten-millionths of an inch.

Such a barrier must have billions of holes of this size or smaller. Furthermore, these holes must not enlarge or plug up as the result of direct corrosion or dust coming from corrosion elsewhere in the system. The barrier must be able to withstand the pressure "head" of one atmosphere. It also had to be of a type that could be manufactured in large quantities and with uniform quality.

It was further realized that thousands of powerful pumps would be needed and thousands of kilowatts to operate them. Also, that the whole circulating system would have to be made vacuum-tight and leakproof, requirements presenting problems of a magnitude never faced before. A new industry had to be developed to manufacture the porous barrier. To satisfy the demands for power, a huge powerhouse was constructed, the largest initial single installation of its kind ever built.

The scientific research work on the diffusion process was initiated by Professor Dunning, and was carried on in a large building in upper Manhattan, under a contract between Columbia University and the Office of Scientific Research and Development (OSRD), until May 1, 1943, when the work was taken over by the Manhattan Engineer District. In 1942 the M. W. Kellogg Company was chosen to plan the large-scale plant. For these purposes that company created a special subsidiary, the Kellex Corporation, and placed P. C. Keith in charge of it. The Kellex Corporation not only planned and procured materials for the large-scale plant, but also carried on research and development in its Jersey City laboratories and with the Columbia group. The plant was constructed by the J. A. Jones Construction Company, of Charlotte, North Carolina. In January 1943 Carbide and Carbon Chemicals Corporation was selected as the operator of the plant. Its engineers soon began to play a large role not only in the planning and construction but also in the research work.

CHAPTER ELEVEN

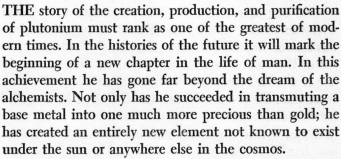

THE story of the creation, production, and purification of plutonium must rank as one of the greatest of modern times. In the histories of the future it will mark the beginning of a new chapter in the life of man. In this achievement he has gone far beyond the dream of the alchemists. Not only has he succeeded in transmuting a base metal into one much more precious than gold; he has created an entirely new element not known to exist under the sun or anywhere else in the cosmos.

Plutonium, element 94, is the child of neptunium, element 93, another man-made element. It is the grandchild of a new isotope of uranium, U.239, which is also artificially produced. Thus in creating plutonium man took three steps beyond nature.

The process of this elemental creation starts in the atomic pile, in which U.238 is mated with U.235. As often happens in the act of propagation of species, the male element, U.235, is destroyed in the consummation of this marriage of the elements. By its very act of death the U.235 liberates the fertilizing agent, the neutron, which penetrates the U.238 nucleus. When this happens, the U.238 also goes out of existence, and a new isotope of uranium is born, containing 147, instead of 146, neutrons.

147

This new isotope has a rather turbulent existence. The nucleus is top-heavy and begins making frantic efforts to restore the balance between protons and neutrons. Soon a negative electron (beta particle) comes flying out. This negative electric particle is lost by one of the 147 neutrons in the U.239 nucleus. That neutron is thus left with its positive charge deneutralized; that is, it has been converted into a proton. In other words, the U.239 again has the original quota of 146 neutrons; but instead of 92 protons, it now has 93.

This means that a new element, element 93, has been created out of element 92. Since uranium was named after the planet Uranus, the element beyond uranium was named neptunium, after the planet Neptune.

But the volcanic eruptions started by the neutron do not end here. Neptunium also has a turbulent life. In a short time the process repeats itself. One of its 146 neutrons radiates away a negative particle and becomes transmuted into a proton. This means that the nucleus now has 94 protons and 145 neutrons. It still has a mass of 239, but it is now an entirely new element, beyond uranium as well as beyond neptunium, a ninety-fourth building block in the cosmic edifice. Following the nomenclature of elements 92 and 93, element 94 was named after the planet Pluto. The great-grandchild of uranium, named after Uranus, god of the heavens, thus bears the name of the god of death.

Strangely enough, the planets Neptune and Pluto, as well as the two elements named after them, entered the realm of being after they had existed for some time in the realm of ideas. The two planets and the two elements are both outstanding examples of the materialization of intellectual concepts. Neptune was discovered first by mathematical calculations, based on a disturbance in the motion of Uranus, which enabled the astronomers Adams and Leverrier to predict correctly not only the existence of the unknown planet but also its size and exact position. Similarly Pluto was discovered following a prediction of its existence by Percival Lowell, also made on the basis of variations in the motion of Uranus. In the same manner, neptunium and plutonium were discovered as the result of predictions, based on the nuclear reactions of uranium with neutrons.

It will be remembered that the whole story of fission came as the direct result of an attempt to create an element beyond uranium. It was another case in which the quest of a passage to the Indies led to the discovery of a new continent. What had been mistakenly believed to be elements 93 and 94, and other elements beyond them, turned out to be fission products of uranium. Yet the hope of creating a true transuranic element was never given up, and the discovery that U.238 absorbed neutrons without being split made it practically certain on theoretical grounds that, while U.235 underwent fission, U.238 was transmuted into a new element, or elements, by fission-liberated neutrons.

However, in spite of many attempts to discover these hypothetical true transuranic elements, no experimental proof of their actual creation could be found during 1939 and the early months of 1940. The difficulties in the way were enormous. There was no pure U.238 or U.235. The best experimental method available was to bombard natural uranium with neutrons by means of the cyclotron. This, of course, led to the fission of the U.235 in the uranium sample and the creation of a host of highly radioactive fission fragments. If in the process some U.238 atoms were transmuted into a transuranic element, the sample was too small to be identified amid the whirlwind of the U.235 fragments.

The transuranic elements were once again plaguing

149

the nuclear chemists and physicists, this time by their absence instead of their presence. Whereas before there had been too many of them to be accounted for legitimately, they had now managed to hide themselves completely in the atomic jungle. From bewildering realities they had changed into elemental ghosts.

As has often happened before in the history of scientific discovery, the first glimpse of the ghost came by chance, but it was the sort of chance that, in the words of Pasteur, "favors the prepared mind." For many months Dr. McMillan and Dr. Abelson had been methodically investigating the fission products of U.235. By means of a technique developed by Dr. Abelson for identifying radioactive substances by their characteristic X-rays, with which he had come very close to the discovery of fission, they had set out to classify the various ingredients in the brew of the fission caldron. At the same time they were not unmindful of the possibility that the mixture might also yield at least one of the elusive transuranium elements.

And sure enough, one day in the spring of 1940 they noticed a newcomer. Unlike the fission products, which recoiled with tremendous energy, this stranger kept apart from them, displaying very little kinetic energy as compared with the others. This indicated at once that it was not a product of fission of U.235, but more likely a new radioactive isotope of uranium, which, not having been split, did not possess the great energy imparted by the broken-up U.235 nucleus to its fragments.

Radioactive elements can be used as tracers. Even amounts so minute that they cannot be seen can be detected through their radioactivity. By using various reagents and precipitants, it can be determined which of these carries the radioactive substance along with it, and this, in turn, provides information on the chemical properties of the unknown radioactive substance.

With such methods Drs. McMillan and Abelson were able to determine, by May 1940, that the unknown radioactive substance was element 93, born through the emission of an electron by U.239, which in turn had been produced by the capture of a neutron by U.238. In their published report, which appeared on June 15, 1940, they also described a method for separating neptunium from the other known elements, based on the chemical properties revealed through tracer quantities of the new element. The report further pointed out that, since neptunium had been observed to emit an electron, "element 94 was certainly present in the neptunium decay product."

They were unable, however, to demonstrate the presence of element 94, since it was present in amounts too minute for detection even by radioactivity. Before they could proceed with this work, Dr. McMillan was called away to work on microwave radar at the newly formed radiation laboratory at the Massachusetts Institute of Technology, Cambridge, Massachusetts, while Dr. Abelson, who had completed his work for his Ph.D., left to take a position with the Carnegie Institution of Washington.

Dr. Glenn T. Seaborg, of the University of California chemistry department, wrote to Dr. McMillan and Dr. Abelson for permission to carry on the work in search of element 94. They not only granted Dr. Seaborg's request, but also turned over to him all their unpublished data and ideas. By December 20, 1940, Dr. Seaborg, in collaboration with Dr. Joseph W. Kennedy and Arthur C. Wahl (at that time a graduate student in chemistry), and with the co-operation of Dr. McMillan through correspondence, succeeded in producing a new substance by the bombardment of uranium with the nuclei of heavy hydrogen (deuterons) fired by the cyclotron. However, at that time the new substance could only be partially identified as element 94.

While this work was in progress in California, a conference of far-reaching import was held at Columbia University on December 15, 1940, between Drs. Fermi, Lawrence, and Emilio Segrè, of the University of California, a former associate of Fermi in Rome. Fermi was at that time already at work on a chain-reacting pile, and he strongly suspected even at that early date that in such a pile the U.238 would be transmuted into plutonium. The implications of this hypothesis were enormous, for it was practically certain that plutonium would have the same fissionable properties as U.235 and would have the tremendous advantage of being separable by chemical means. In a word, it would mean that fissionable material could be produced in the quantities necessary for atomic bombs.

The work of McMillan and Abelson in creating neptunium, and particularly their observation that it emitted electrons and thus was most likely transmuted into element 94, furnished the first experimental proof that the hypothesis was correct. Only one more step was necessary to make the evidence conclusive—to make actual observations of the transmutation. This would require performing the McMillan-Abelson experiments on a much larger scale, so that a sufficient amount of element 94 (it had not yet been named) would be produced.

This, in substance, was the subject of the conference that day at Columbia University. It led to the momentous decision to push the work on 94 as vigorously as possible. It was further realized that, in order to reproduce conditions that would prevail in the pile, it would

152

be necessary to use neutrons, instead of deuterons, as the particles for bombarding uranium.

On March 1, 1941 Drs. Seaborg, Segrè, Kennedy, and Lawrence proceeded to bombard about one kilogram of uranium with neutrons. It was the largest amount of any substance ever subjected to bombardment by the cyclotron. For six days and nights this terrific bombardment against the citadel of the uranium nucleus was carried on. On March 6 they succeeded. As in the McMillan-Abelson experiments, the uranium had been transmuted into neptunium. And, beautiful to behold, they found that the neptunium had in turn, by the emission of an electron, been metamorphosed into a new element. The newcomer announced his arrival by a shower of alpha particles, telltale radiations that theory had predicted as characteristic of element 94, plutonium.

Man had produced the first made-to-order element in history, but the great test was yet to come. By March 28 about one half of a microgram of plutonium 239 had been produced. This the scientists proceeded to bombard with slow neutrons to determine whether it was subject to fission in the same degree as U.235. On that day a tense group stood around the oscilloscope. They saw the ionization pulses in the atomic thermometer rise to the same peaks produced by the fission of U.235.

The news traveled quickly to the Uranium Committee in Washington. It reached the physics laboratory at Columbia University. It gave the Atomic Bomb Project, at that time still tentative, a new impetus and a new direction.

Work then proceeded vigorously on the production of further amounts of plutonium. To increase the yield it became highly desirable to procure some metallic uranium, practically non-existent at that time. On consulting Professor Gilbert N. Lewis, it was learned that some fourteen years before, one of his students, a native of Sweden, had prepared a fairly large sample of metallic uranium of a high degree of purity. No one knew what had become of the uranium or of the student. Through the Swedish Legation it was learned that he had returned to Sweden. An urgent cable was sent to him asking the whereabouts of the precious metal. Came back the reply: "In Professor Lewis's desk." It had been there for fourteen years.

As the result of the discovery of neptunium and plutonium, Drs. Seaborg and M. L. Perlman made a search for these elements in pitchblende and found evidence of the existence of plutonium to the extent of about one part to 100,000 billion parts of pitchblende by weight. They ascribe this amount present in the ore as being due to the continuous absorption by U.238 of an appreciable fraction of the neutrons that are continually emitted during the spontaneous fission of uranium. This indicates that plutonium is also being constantly created in nature, the only known example of creation still going on.

When the building of plutonium-producing piles was under consideration in 1942, some of the scientists feared that it might take too long to work out the chemical procedures for its separation. Dr. Seaborg, however, felt confident that it could be done in a reasonable time.

Since no more than microgram amounts could be made by the cyclotron, Seaborg and his associates started work on the ultramicro scale. The first plutonium in the form of a compound was isolated on August 18, 1942, by Drs. B. B. Cunningham and L. B. Werner, and a number of further compounds were made a month later. On the basis of these "bits of nothing" they proceeded to design a huge chemical plant to scale, the microgram amounts serving as a pilot plant for actual operations some ten billion times greater in scope.

154

To do so they had to use a host of other chemicals in exact proportions, in quantities of micrograms and fractions of micrograms, within a limit of accuracy of three per cent. (A human breath weighs about 750,000 micrograms.) To achieve this unheard-of accuracy in weighing, an ultramicro balance of an extremely high sensitivity was designed and built by P. L. Kirk and R. D. Craig of the University of California. This balance could weigh amounts as small as a microgram with an accuracy of three per cent, and could actually weigh a mass as small as 0.03 micrograms.

Work continued on approximately this scale of operation until about January 1944, at which time milligram amounts of plutonium became available. There soon followed experiments on the gram and then on the ten-gram scale. Following these the scale became substantially larger.

On the basis of these ultramicro-scale procedures a large pilot plant was built at the Clinton Engineer Works, where the chemistry for concentrating and purifying plutonium was further developed under the direction of Professor Warren Johnson, of the University of Chicago, and Major Oswald H. Greager, formerly of the du Pont Company.

Before this pilot plant was completed, however, work began on three huge separation plants at the Hanford Engineer Works. These plants, rectangular structures 800 feet long, are the most remarkable chemical factories ever conceived or designed. In them enormous quantities of materials are made to go through complicated chemical processes with no human eye ever seeing what actually goes on except through an intricate series of dials and panels that enable the operators to maintain perfect control of every single operation at all times. Each operation is performed in a remote cell behind thick walls, and when it is completed the treated material invisibly moves on to the next cell, until at the end of a series of such passages the miracle of modern alchemy emerges, ready for the next stage on its ultimate journey. The remote-control operation was made necessary because the plutonium comes associated with the fission products of U.235, which emit an amount of radiation that would be lethal to any life in its vicinity.

Hanford Engineer Works is located in Benton County, in the south-central portion of the state of Washington, between the Yakima Range and the Columbia River. It lies on the undulating tableland containing for the most part a desolate region of gray sand, gray-green sagebrush, and dried watercourses. The region is drained by the Columbia River, east of the Cascades, where the Rattlesnake Hills, Saddle Mountains, and Yakima Range form the inland extremities of that system and constitute a plant barricade to the south, north, and west. The nearest community of any size is Yakima, some forty miles westward, which has a normal population of about 30,000.

The manufacturing area lies entirely on the south, or right, bank of the Columbia River, which bounds it to the north and northwest. The manufacturing reservation is nearly level, broken prominently only by Cable Mountain, an outcropping of basalt that underlies the entire site, usually at a considerable depth. The overburden consists of a poorly cemented shale and sandstone stratum known as the Ellensburg Formation, above which are deposits of sand and gravel, chiefly alluvial.

The area owned or controlled through lease amounts to approximately 631 square miles. Of this total, 230 square miles are owned by the Government. The manufacturing reservation contains 195 square miles. The remaining area is accounted for by the purchase of power and irrigation properties and rights, and by the acquisition of Richland Village, to the south of the manufacturing area, as a site for the housing development and the administration center. Leased property is either on a basis of no occupancy or controlled occupancy as warranted by considerations of safety and security. For the protection of employees and the public generally, monitor stations are strategically located in the operating and service areas, and outside the limits of land owned and leased.

The manufacturing area is divided into three huge sections, and each of these three is subdivided into subsections covering miles of ground. One of the three main areas contains the three great chain-reacting piles for the production of plutonium. The second area contains the three chemical plants where the plutonium is separated and concentrated. The third area is where the raw material for the plutonium piles is prepared.

The three piles are located on the south bank of the Columbia River at the northern extremity of the manufacturing reservation. Each of the piles is bounded by some 4.1 miles of fence, overlooked by guard towers located, at most, 2,000 feet apart. Within the fence lie some 685 acres of land, 4.25 miles of broad-gauge track, and 6.75 miles of roads.

The three plants are completely self-contained. Each is about seven to eight miles distant from the next one. The nearest to Richland Village is thirty miles away.

The construction of the Hanford Engineer Works presented innumerable and unprecedented problems, which stemmed from several basic requirements established by research and development, engineering design, and policy. The principal factors that created these problems were: the magnitude of the project; the distances between the several manufacturing plants to be con-

157

structed; the isolated location of the site; the time element, which demanded that construction proceed without awaiting completion of engineering design; the unusually high quality of construction required in many instances; and the extreme and rigid requirements of military secrecy.

The magnitude of the work of construction is indicated by the following general items selected at random: Excavation amounted to 25,000,000 cubic yards of earth, a quantity approximately one fourth of the earth moved in the construction of the Fort Peck Dam, the largest earth dam ever constructed. A total of 40,000 carloads of material were received on the site, equivalent to a train 333 miles long. More than 780,000 cubic yards of concrete were placed, an amount approximately equal to 390 miles of concrete highway twenty feet wide and six inches thick. Excluding railroad rail and special steels, about 40,000 tons of steel were used in building construction. Approximately 160,000,000 board feet of lumber were required, equivalent to the yield from 135 acres of the best timberland. About 1,500,000 concrete blocks and 750,000 cement bricks were used in plant construction; more than 11,000 poles were required for the electric power and lighting systems; more than 8,500 pieces of construction equipment were used. Approximately 345 miles of permanent plant roads were constructed on the site.

The necessity for separating the several areas from each other and from inhabited localities by relatively great distances imposed abnormal problems for the transportation of men and materials. These distances are emphasized by the fact that 340,000,000 passenger-miles of bus transportation were furnished during the construction phase of the work.

The isolation of the site from any existing centers of

158

population presented serious problems with respect to many phases of construction. These were related primarily to the procurement, transportation, housing, feeding, health, morale, and retention of a maximum total construction force of about 45,000 persons, a total reached in June 1944.

The urgent need for putting the plant in operation at the earliest possible date made it necessary in a number of instances to proceed with construction before basic research had been fully developed. Steps had to be taken that, in the words of Professor Smyth, "no engineer or scientist in his right mind would consider in peacetime," and could be justified even in wartime only by the "possibility of achieving tremendously important results."

There is as much difference between the first chain-reacting pile at Chicago and the giant plutonium piles at the Hanford Engineer Works as there is between a toy popgun and a battery of the most powerful modern artillery. Essentially they are both latticeworks of graphite and uranium, in which a chain reaction perpetuates itself through the liberation of neutrons by the fission of U.235 in unseparated uranium, and the slowing down of the neutrons in the graphite. But, by comparison, the first is a crude shack alongside the Empire State Building.

The actual size and power of the Hanford piles cannot be given. Nevertheless, some relative data may prove illuminating. Before building the piles at Hanford a small, experimental pile was constructed at the Clinton Engineer Works to serve as a pilot plant. As it turned out, the Hanford piles were designed along different engineering lines, but for purposes of comparison the Clinton pile is much closer to the ones at Hanford than to the Chicago prototype. Originally designed to operate at a power of a 1,000 kilowatts, which corresponds to the splitting of less than one milligram of U.235 per day, it reached a power level of 1,800 kilowatts in May 1944. This Clinton pile was thus 9,000 times more powerful than the Chicago pile. Yet it is a mere pygmy alongside any of the Hanford giants.

The construction of these mammoth atomic piles required the solution of many problems of a type and a scale never encountered before. The first problem, of course, was to design a practical plant that would produce plutonium in sufficient quantities for atomic bombs. This end could not be achieved by merely scaling up the Chicago model, as it would have taken five million of these to produce just one kilogram a day. Hence the design had to be of a radically different nature, not merely larger in size.

A pile in which large quantities of U.235 are being split generates radiations equivalent to those of tons of radium. Hence the piles had to be surrounded by concrete walls several feet thick. Since these radiations are greater by far than anything ever encountered before, they created one of the greatest health problems ever faced. To meet the challenge, a staff of several hundred of the country's leading radiologists, under the direction of Colonel Warren and Dr. R. S. Stone, was organized to carry out pioneer studies in this unknown field and to devise new methods for the effective protection of all personnel.

The greater the power at which the pile is operated, the greater is the energy liberated in the form of heat. This heat is equivalent to that of burning 3,000,000 kilograms of coal per kilogram of U.235 used up in fission, and if not efficiently carried off, it might vaporize the pile and lead to the greatest of catastrophes. The cooling problem was one of the most difficult that faced the designers of the pile. It had at first been decided to use helium as the coolant. For various reasons it was finally decided to use water.

This created enormous engineering problems. To carry off the amounts of heat generated in the pile would require the circulation of a quantity of water large enough to supply a fair-sized city. Furthermore, since this water would become hot, it in turn would have to be cooled before it was returned to the Columbia River, as otherwise it might raise the temperature of the river to a point incompatible with fish life. If it was decided that the water could go through the system only once, a huge retention basin would have to be designed so as to allow the radioactivity induced in the water to die down before the water could be returned to the river.

The decision to use water as the coolant also opened up another serious problem. To load and unload the pile, the uranium is shaped in the form of cylinders, which are inserted in channels passing through the graphite. When enough plutonium has accumulated in the cylinders, they are pushed out by remote control into a deep water basin in the rear of the pile, whence they are transferred to the chemical separation plant.

Since the heat develops in the uranium, the water would have to circulate in contact with it through the channels in the graphite. The indications were that the uranium would react chemically with the water, probably to the point of disintegrating the uranium cylinders. Hence it became necessary to seal the uranium in a protective can made of a material that had to meet a number of stringent requirements: it must not absorb too many neutrons; it had to transmit heat from the uranium to the water; it had to protect uranium from water corrosion; it had to withstand the terrific heat; it had to have a high resistance against the radiations; and it had to keep fission products out of the water. The failure of a

161

single can might result in putting an entire pile out of operation.

The problem of the can proved to be one of the most difficult to solve. Professor Smyth reports that on his periodic visits to Chicago, where the problem was being studied along with the other problems relating to the pile, "he could roughly estimate the state of the canning problem by the atmosphere of gloom or joy he found around the laboratory." Aluminum had been decided on as the material best suited for the purpose, but several very troublesome problems still remained. It proved very difficult to get a uniform, heat-conducting bond between the aluminum and the uranium. Nor was it found possible to effect a gas-tight closure for the can. The final solution did not come until October 1944, after the first Hanford pile had begun operations.

Another problem involved the radioactive gases developed as fission products in the pile. High stacks were built to carry them off, but since the behavior of these gases is dependent on the weather, meteorological studies were made over a period of many months to determine whether the stack gases would be likely to spread radioactive fission products in dangerous concentrations. The studies, made at both Clinton and Hanford, led to the working out of specifications for the operation of the stacks.

The energy from the piles is heating the Columbia River, but the actual rise in temperature is so small that no effect was to be expected on fish life. A series of elaborate experiments confirmed this expectation.

The Hanford piles are the first atomic power plants built on earth, atomic boilers generating enormous amounts of atomic energy in the form of heat. In these boilers atoms by the trillions are ripped asunder and new elements are constantly being created. Many of these, fission products distinct from plutonium, have great potential value in biology, medicine, and industry.

Thus the atomic pile is actually a three-in-one plant: It creates large quantities of plutonium. It produces a host of valuable new radioactive elements. It liberates a vast amount of atomic energy, which today goes to heat the Columbia, but promises more utilitarian applications for tomorrow.

To behold these atomic power plants standing in their primeval majesty is one of the most terrifying and awe-inspiring spectacles on earth today. There is not a sign, not the slightest hint, that within these huge man-made blocks titanic cosmic fires are raging such as had never raged on earth in its present form. One stands before them as though beholding the realization of a vision such as Michelangelo might have had of a world yet to be, as indescribable as the Grand Canyon of Arizona, Beethoven's Ninth Symphony, or the presence "whose dwelling is the light of setting suns."

In these Promethean structures, which may well stand as eternal monuments to the spirit of man challenging nature, mighty cosmic forces are at work such as had never been let loose on this planet in the million years of man's existence on its surface, and probably never in the two billion years of the earth's being. Here, for the first time in history, man stands in the presence of the very act of elemental creation of matter. Here in the great silences—for the plants operate in a stillness where even the beating of one's heart can be heard—new elements are being born, a phenomenon that, as far as man knows, has not happened since Genesis.

This development no doubt will rank in the future story of mankind as a definite landmark, signalizing a new cultural age, the Age of Atomics, or of Nucleonics, as some scientists prefer to designate it. For this there is

163

no parallel. All the great ages—the Iron Age, the Bronze Age, the ages of steam and electricity, each of which revolutionized conditions of living—arrived imperceptibly, and man did not become aware of them until their effects were fully felt. This marks the first time in the history of man's struggle to bend the forces of nature to his will that he is actually present at the birth of a new era on this planet, with full awareness of its titanic potentialities for good or evil.

One is reassured on seeing the most remarkable system of automatic controls, and controls of controls, devised to keep this man-made Titan from breaking his bonds. Left without control for even a few seconds, the giant would run wild. Enormous as the mass is, its mechanisms and controls are adjusted with the fineness of the most delicate jeweled watch, and they respond with the sensitiveness of a fine Stradivarius. The slightest deviation from normal behavior, and the automatic controls go into operation. They can stop the Titan in his tracks almost instantly.

CHAPTER TWELVE

AS early as March 1939, only about a month after the announcement of the discovery of fission in this country, Dr. Fermi went to Washington to arouse the interest of our Army and Navy in the possible use of fission for military purposes. In a conference with representatives of the Navy Department, he suggested the possibility of achieving either a controllable reaction with slow neutrons, or an uncontrolled reaction, producing an explosion of a magnitude previously undreamed of, with fast neutrons.

It was recognized that the amount of U.235 that would be necessary to make a bomb would not be very large, as in pure U.235 the principal competitor for the available neutrons—namely, U.238—would not be present, and hence most of the neutrons liberated through fission would go into producing further fissions; and since these are fast neutrons, the fissions would take place at an incredibly rapid rate, producing an explosion of cataclysmic dimensions.

However, in a mass of U.235, neutrons would be lost by escape into the outer air, and if too many of them were to be lost in this way, the combustion of the U.235 atoms—that is, fission—would die out like a fire that lacks air. Since, as explained earlier, the production of

165

neutrons, which is a volume effect, will increase more rapidly with size than the loss by escape into the air, which is a surface effect, this loss by escape can be reduced by increasing the size of the mass to the point at which enough neutrons will be liberated and retained inside the mass to produce the explosion. This means that no explosion can take place unless you have a minimum mass of material, a minimum known as the critical size.

It can thus be seen that an atomic explosion is very different in its mechanism from the ordinary chemical explosion of TNT and other explosives. In these, any quantity, no matter how small, can be exploded, while no quantity, no matter how large, will explode by itself if the proper precautions are taken. In atomic material, however, the explosion can occur only if the quantity reaches this critical amount. Quantities of the material less than the critical amount are perfectly stable and safe. On the other hand, a quantity greater than this critical amount will go off automatically by itself, and no power on earth can stop it.

I can therefore reveal to you the principal secret of the atomic bomb: all you have to do to explode an atomic bomb is to unite at great rapidity two pieces of the active material, each smaller than the critical amount, but exceeding it when brought together. As Dr. Robert Williams, one of the earliest scientists to arrive at the atomic bomb center at Los Alamos put it: "Take some fissionable material in several pieces, as pure as possible, and slap them together as quickly as possible."

This, however, is not so simple as it sounds. As the British statement points out, if an appreciable fraction of the atoms of U.235 undergo fission within a very short time, the amount of energy liberated will be so great that the mass will attain a temperature of "many million degrees and a pressure of many millions of atmospheres."

166

It will consequently expand with very great rapidity. As the density of the mass decreases, the neutrons can escape more easily from it, and the chain reaction will come to end.

In order to release an appreciable fraction of the available energy, it is therefore necessary that the reaction should develop so rapidly that a substantial part of the material can react before the system has time to fly apart. The neutrons produced in the fission process are fast enough to fulfill this condition, but not if the neutrons are artificially slowed down.

How, then, can subcritical masses of U.235 be brought together rapidly enough to avoid predetonation? Here is atomic bomb secret number two: shoot one part as a projectile in a gun against a second part as a target.

This, again, is not too easy, of course. As Professor Smyth points out, the projectile mass, projectile speed, and gun caliber required were not far from the range of standard ordnance practice, but novel problems were introduced by the importance of achieving sudden and perfect contact between projectile and target, by the use of a tamper to reflect escaping neutrons back into the mass, and by the requirement of portability.

In these last two phrases are revealed more vital secrets of the atomic bomb. This requires some explanation.

The critical size of a uranium-graphite pile, as well as that of an atomic bomb, may be considerably reduced by an envelope made of a substance that reflects neutrons. In a chain-reacting pile this envelope consists of a layer of graphite. In the case of the bomb the most effective envelope is a substance having a high density. Such a neutron-reflecting envelope is known as a tamper.

In the bomb such a tamper not only reduces the critical size, thus saving precious material, but also plays an additional part: its very inertia, as Professor Smyth points out, delays the expansion of the active substance, and makes for a longer-lasting, more energetic, and more efficient explosion. By a fortunate coincidence, materials of high density are also excellent as reflectors for neutrons.

Since gold is one of those materials, it was at one time seriously contemplated putting some of the gold hoard buried at Fort Knox to work in the atomic bomb, just as the idle silver in the Treasury was put to work in one of the plants for concentrating the U.235 for the bomb.

Here, then, is the third secret of the atomic bomb: the use of an envelope surrounding the active material as a tamper, to decrease the critical size and greatly to increase the bomb's efficiency.

Secret number four is that this tamper is made of material of high density. Gold is such a material, if anyone wants to blow it up, which may be all that it will be good for in case of a war with atomic bombs.

Secret number five is of course easily guessed at: portability. Since the atomic bomb had to be dropped from a bomber, its weight and shape had to be within the limits of what a B-29 could carry. Since the maximum load for a B-29 from the Marianas to Japan was ten tons, it is obvious that the atomic bomb could not have a total weight of more than that maximum.

How much is the critical amount? This is still one of the great secrets, but even here an approximation within rather narrow limits can be made. In the summer of 1940 a figure of one to one hundred kilograms of U.235 was commonly given as the critical size of the bomb.

Now, President Truman has stated that the bomb that wiped out Hiroshima "had more power than 20,000 tons of TNT." According to the figure given in the Official Report, one kilogram of U.235, if all the atoms in it underwent fission, would release energy equivalent to the explosion of 20,000 short tons of TNT. Hence, if the

168

efficiency of the explosion over Hiroshima was one hundred per cent, the active material in that bomb weighed no more than one kilogram (2.2 pounds). If the efficiency of the nuclear explosion was only one per cent, then the amount of the material used was one hundred kilograms.

On the other hand, the Official Report states on page 63 that by the end of 1941 "it was predicted that possibly ten per cent of the total energy might be released explosively." On the basis of that prediction (which may or may not have proved to be true), the critical amount of the Hiroshima bomb was ten kilograms.

Suppose the critical amount was found to be 100 kilograms. Anything below that amount would therefore be perfectly stable and safe; no power on earth could make it explode. Hence we divide the 100 kilograms into two parts, let's say, of seventy and thirty kilograms respectively. We assemble these two parts in a high-speed gun in which the heavier part will serve as the target and the lighter as the projectile. When the two are far enough apart, they are, of course, harmless.

When the time comes to explode it, a mechanism is set to make the gun go off at a certain predetermined distance from the ground. When that happens, the projectile hits the target and brings the two parts together. A critical mass is formed and there is one less city in the world. As soon as the parts join, the neutrons build up so rapidly that the explosion takes place in about one tenth of a millionth of a second.

One more secret may be cleared up. The bomb was not dropped by parachute, as is commonly believed. It was dropped free. It is true that the Japanese saw something drop by parachute and thus gave rise to the common misconception, but what they saw were instruments dropped by parachutes from the accompanying plane to make blast measurements. It was through these instruments that President Truman was able to state as a fact that the bomb "had more power than 20,000 tons of TNT."

How much does the entire assembly weigh? The exact amount is being kept secret, but it may be said that it weighs several tons and, as General Farrell has stated in a public address, "it substantially fills the bomb bay of a B-29."

The bomb is detonated in combat at such a height above the ground as to give the maximum blast effect against structures, and to disseminate the radioactive products as a cloud. On account of the height of the explosion, as the War Department pointed out, "practically all the radioactive products are carried upward in the ascending column of hot air and dispersed harmlessly over a wide area. Even in the New Mexico test, where the height of explosion was necessarily low, only a very small fraction of the radioactivity was deposited immediately below the bomb."

While the energy released in the fission of all the atoms in a kilogram of U.235 is equivalent to that of 20,000 tons of TNT, this energy represents the conversion of only one thousandth of the mass—namely, one gram—into energy. The conversion of one gram of matter into energy thus produces the equivalent of 20,000 tons of TNT. Since the bomb dropped over Hiroshima had a power of about 20,000 tons, it means that the destruction of that city was caused by the conversion into energy of only one gram of matter.

This conversion took place in one tenth of a millionth of a second, or at a rate of 10,000,000 million grams, more than 10,000 tons, per second.

As the sun, which produces its radiation by the conversion of matter into energy, is one third of a million times the mass of the earth, the sun should be converting its matter at the rate of 3,000 million tons per second. Since it does this at the rate of only 4 million tons per second, the conversion of the matter in the Hiroshima bomb was at a rate 750 times faster than the rate at which energy in the sun is created out of matter.

In that one tenth of a millionth of a second vast cosmic forces are set in motion, attained, as far as our present knowledge goes, only in the super exploding stars known as super-novæ, giant stellar bodies vastly greater than our sun, which, for some unknown reason, explode in interstellar space and shine with the light of a billion suns for a relatively short time.

The temperature at the time of the atomic explosion at Hiroshima, according to testimony before the Special Committee on Atomic Energy of the United States Senate by Dr. Philip Morrison, one of our brilliant young nuclear physicists, reached 100,000,000 degrees Fahrenheit (55,000,000 degrees centigrade) in its center. This is about three times as great as the temperature estimated for the interior of the sun, and nearly ten thousand times the temperature of the sun's surface. To attain an internal temperature of such magnitude would require a star with the luminosity of 400,000,000 suns, or 400 ordinary novæ combined into one.

The pressure attained during an atomic explosion is even more staggering in its dimensions, reaching hundreds of billions of atmospheres. The energy generated by an atomic bomb at the time of explosion, calculated on the basis of ten per cent efficiency, is enough to raise the entire United States wartime fleet of 9,000,000 displacement tons nearly two miles into the air.

At this point some misconception must be cleared up as to the total maximum amount of fission energy in a given mass available for the explosion, which must not be confused with the total amount of energy actually contained

171

in that mass if all the matter in it were to be converted into energy, according to the Einstein formula for the equivalence of mass and energy. The maximum amount of fission energy available for an explosion in any given mass of U.235 or plutonium is only one tenth of one per cent of the total energy contained in that mass. If we state, for example, that one kilogram of U.235, when exploding with one hundred per cent efficiency, would release energy equivalent to 20,000 short tons of TNT, that amount would represent only one tenth of one per cent, or one thousandth part, of the total energy contained in that kilogram. In other words, the total amount of energy present in that kilogram, on the basis of the Einstein formula (see Chapter II), if all its matter could be converted into energy, would be the equivalent of 20,-000,000 short tons of TNT. In the process of fission, however, only one thousandth part of the matter is converted into energy. Furthermore, this one thousandth of the total energy is all that we can get or ever will get out of uranium or plutonium. It represents one hundred per cent of the total energy available for the explosion. If we state that the explosion went off with ten per cent efficiency we mean one tenth of one thousandth, not one tenth of the total energy in the entire mass.

That is the way nature has arranged it, and there is nothing man can do about it. All he can do is to take advantage of what nature has given him and use her bounty up to the limit—that is, one tenth of one per cent, which in the case of uranium and plutonium would be a full one hundred per cent of the total energy available for man's use.

The reason for this is not hard to find. Every unit of atomic mass is the equivalent in energy of 1,000,000,000 (one billion) electron volts (an electron volt is a very small fraction of an erg, unit of work). Since an atom of

172

U.235 is composed of 235 such units, the total mass of the atom of U.235 has an energy equivalent of 235,000,-000,000 electron volts. But in the process of fission only 200,000,000 electron volts of energy are liberated; that is, only one fifth of a unit of mass of the 235 units in the atom, or $\frac{1}{1,175}$ of the atom's mass, is converted into energy. This is roughly only $\frac{1}{12}$ per cent, but in round figures it is generally given as $\frac{1}{10}$ of one per cent—namely, one part per thousand.

It cannot be overemphasized that this rather small percentage is the maximum available. That is all there is; no power known to man can make the atom yield the slightest bit more. It is just as immutable a law of nature as is the law of gravitation, and we can no more change it than we can change the pull of gravity at a given point.

But this small amount is certainly a tremendous trifle. To illustrate: A bomb containing one hundred kilograms of U.235, if all its atoms were to undergo fission, would liberate the energy equivalent to 2,000,000 short tons of TNT. If only ten per cent of its atoms undergo fission, the energy liberated would still be the equivalent of 200,000 tons of TNT, or ten times more powerful than the bomb dropped on Hiroshima.

Thus the power of the bomb can be increased either by increasing its size or by improving its efficiency, or both. Since the bomb dropped on Nagasaki, three days after the Hiroshima bomb, made the first one obsolete, there can be little doubt that within the next ten years we may expect to have atomic bombs of a power equivalent to 100,000 to 250,000 tons of TNT. Such bombs, particularly if used in quantity, will destroy not only cities but whole areas. They could cripple a nation and destroy its power of resistance in a few minutes.

Such bombs, of course, will not be carried by airplane.

173

Long-range rockets, using atomic energy for fuel, could travel to any part of the globe at speeds of thousands of miles per hour, at altitudes of several hundred miles. It would even be impossible under these circumstances to tell where these rockets came from. The nation attacked would be staggering in the dark in a frantic effort to find out who the enemy was. The friendliness of a nation would be no guarantee of innocence, since the diplomacy of the atomic age would call for the outward appearance of the utmost friendliness to avert suspicion when the atomic bombs began to fall.

A nation starting such an atomic war would not necessarily do so because it was bent on aggression. Living in constant fear, day by day, hour by hour, minute by minute, and second by second, that at any moment a rain of atomic bombs might come from somewhere, the tension must sooner or later become unendurable. It would take only a few, trigger-happy men at the push-buttons to start pushing them frantically in the conviction that by doing so they were only beating the other fellows to the push. The nation to start it would most likely be the one whose nerves were the first to crack under the strain. The start of an atomic war would thus probably be an expression of a primitive, animal-like fear of the unknown. Unless he takes wise measures in time, and that means now, man of the atomic age will by force of necessity revert to the animal. He will retrogress 500,-000 years, all the way back to the cave he started from, except that this time he will have the means to annihilate himself.

On the other hand, since, as Professor Oppenheimer pointed out, atomic bombs of the future will be cheap, plentiful, and easy to make, small nations will have them as well as large. Hence, if atomic bombs begin to pour down from the sky some dark night, the responsibility could by no means be pinned on any one, or on several, of the small number of great industrial powers. Since these powers would have much more to lose from an atomic bomb war, it would be more likely that an ambitious military clique that had gained control over a small nation, as is the case with Argentina, Spain, and several other small powers, might decide the time had come for them to have their fling at the dice of destiny, with everything to gain and rather little to lose.

Man collectively may become Ishmael, a "wild man"; "his hand will be against every man, and every man's hand against him."

PART THREE

Armageddon

CHAPTER THIRTEEN

THE point in space where the atomic bomb was born is now known to the world as Los Alamos. As in the case of Oak Ridge, there was no town by that name on that spot. At the beginning there was only a canyon, named Los Alamos, after its poplars, by its Spanish discoverers. More recently the large mesa overlooking the canyon became the site of the Los Alamos Ranch School for boys, where the pupils, if they had a mind to, could do their algebra on horseback.

Los Alamos is only one of many breath-taking canyons, separated by mesas with steeply sloping sides, often dropping abruptly a sheer hundred and fifty feet to the treetops or brush on the canyon's floor. South of Los Alamos are several other canyons, running parallel to each other on an east-west line to the Rio Grande—Pajarito, Water, Frijoles, Bayo, Pueblo, Guaje, Valle, and Sandia canyons, all part of Los Alamos. Among the plateaus are One-mile Mesa and Two-mile Mesa, South Mesa and Upper South Mesa. A large ranch west of Parajito Canyon, named Anchor Ranch, served as the proving ground for the gun assembly of the bomb.

As the crow flies, Los Alamos lies twenty-five miles northwest of Santa Fe, but there is no way of getting there by a straight route. One must first drive twenty-five miles north to the ancient little Spanish-American town of Espanola, then turn back and drive in a southwesterly direction over a tortuous road that winds its way for sixteen miles through the tableland overlooking the precipitous canyons to one's right. This road was only a trail when it was taken over by the atomic scientists. Over it, night and day, came a steady procession of trucks carrying cyclotrons and betatrons, Cockcroft-Walton proton accelerators, and Van de Graaff high-voltage spheres, special gadgets made in hundreds of plants and universities throughout the land, crates of U.235 from all the plants at Oak Ridge, and cargoes of plutonium from the giant piles at Hanford.

Over this road traveled, incognito, many of the world's great. On it were carried the finished products for Alamogordo, Hiroshima, and Nagasaki. It was only a little road, but during the summer of 1945 it became one of the world's great highways. On it traveled the substance that changed the course of history.

But for this road, Los Alamos is inaccessible to the outside world. The Jemez Mountains surround it on the west and the Sangre de Cristo Range, with the Truchas Peaks rising to a height of 13,800 feet, to the east. Deep canyons bar the approaches from the north and south. All about are monuments of the great past, Indian, Spanish, Mexican, American. To the north are prehistoric ruins. The Cliff Dwelling Ruins of the Bandelier National Monument are to the south. From Frijoles Canyon westward through the Jemez Mountains is the Valle Grande, the largest extinct volcano ever found, its crater fifteen miles in diameter. Past Cochiti and Santo Domingo Indian pueblos to the southwest is the old ghost town of Bland. To the east across the Rio Grande is the northern end of Jornada del Muerto, the Journey of Death. As one progresses from Santa Fe to

180

Espanola, one somehow crosses the line from today to yesterday. Somewhere between Espanola and Los Alamos one floats across the gap between yesterday and tomorrow. One suddenly finds oneself transported into the twenty-first century.

Geographically Los Alamos sprawls across 45,000 acres. Its center of gravity is on the mesa between Los Alamos and Pueblo canyons. Here, surrounded by a heavily guarded barbed-wire fence, is the Technical Area, where the principal research laboratories and plants are located. In addition to the Tech Area, as it was known, there were twenty other projects, built on the narrow ridges between the canyons, with some located in the canyons themselves.

In the summer of 1945 the Tech Area contained 37 buildings, while the structures on the other sites numbered 201. In addition there were 49 administrative buildings, 52 buildings for the military personnel, 302 apartment buildings containing 620 apartment units, 200 trailers and 52 dormitories. The population consisted of 4,000 civilian and 2,000 military personnel, in command of Colonel Gerald R. Tyler. No place in the world was more heavily guarded than Los Alamos. Its very existence was a top secret. At Hanford and at Oak Ridge it was known among the chosen few as Site-Y. It was the only place where mail was censored and telephone conversations listened in on. Unlike Oak Ridge and Richland, it had no post office. Letters to the outside world were handed unsealed to the intelligence officer, who read them and forwarded them to Santa Fe. If they contained objectionable matter, they were given back to the sender. Letters to Los Alamos were addressed to P.O. Box 1539, Santa Fe, New Mexico.

The population in Los Alamos was divided into two distinct classes, each identified by a badge. The mark

181

of the highest distinction was a white badge, given only to the top scientists. The white badge, accompanied by an identification card, admitted one to the inner circle and to the various sanctums on the place, including the sanctum sanctorum where the bomb was assembled.

By the summer of 1945 the vast majority of the scientists had lived with their families at Los Alamos for about two and a half years. As far as the world knew, they had vanished completely, lost without a trace. Arriving at the place and finding them all there gave one the sensation of discovering a lost world. The mountains and the canyons and the mesas provided the perfect setting for such a world.

One would descend a steep canyon and find a large structure half buried in the ground. Inside the building were men working with the most explosive material on earth.

I shall never forget my visit to the building where the Harvard cyclotron was installed. There in front of the apparatus was a huge pile of little cubes. I casually picked one up.

"What's this?" I asked Professor Robert R. Wilson, who was in charge of the work.

"U.235," he answered.

I looked at the pile. There was enough there to wipe out a city, but the fact that it was cut up in little cubes, separated here and there by neutron-absorbers, kept the mass from becoming critical.

Professor Wilson aroused me from the state of catalepsy that the pile had produced in me by inviting me to the next room for tea, brewed in a chemical retort. Calmly drinking tea out of a chemical retort while an atomic volcano is erupting in the next room is but one example of the atmosphere in which people lived and worked at Los Alamos.

OF THE ATOMIC BOMB

Los Alamos was the land of the free fast neutron, where one wanted, not to tame it, but, on the contrary, to give it full freedom of action. On these mesas, and down below in the canyons, the neutron ruled the lives of the people. At Hanford it was a slave, imprisoned in a moderator and shorn of most of its strength. At Los Alamos the fast neutron was king.

The principal job at Hanford was to maintain a chain reaction with slow neutrons and put them to work transmuting U.238 into plutonium. At Los Alamos the principal job was to devise means whereby fast un-trammeled neutrons would annihilate the plutonium, or U.235, by liberating its energy through an explosion consuming the shortest possible time. The purpose, in other words, was to create the conditions in which the free untamed neutron could do its work in the most efficient manner contrivable.

This was not a job for physicists and explosive experts alone. It required the co-operative efforts of metallurgists and chemists, mathematicians and astrophysicists, engineers and authorities on ballistics, nuclear physicists and nuclear chemists, theoretical scientists and experimentalists, long-hairs and short-hairs. In fact, one of the significant outcomes of the Atomic Bomb Project, and particularly the Los Alamos branch, was the bringing together into a smoothly functioning team of the long-hairs and the short-hairs, who in normal peacetime used to growl at each other from a safe distance. Each learned to respect and admire the other. Oppie, as Dr. Oppenheimer was affectionately called in white-badge and blue-badge circles alike, would, by prewar concepts, have been classed as a long-hair. He is one of the top-flight theoretical physicists now living. In his undergraduate days at Harvard he contributed excellent poetry to one of the advanced literary periodicals. As Dr.

Arthur K. Solomon of Harvard says of him in *Why Smash Atoms?* "he has a peculiar power of self-absorption, and the tales of his absent-mindedness are legion." Yet when called upon to organize the greatest laboratory ever established anywhere, in which success depended on long-hairs and short-hairs working together in harmony, this absent-minded scholar, who now finds the outlet for his poetic vision through higher mathematics, turned out, in his very quiet and soft-spoken way, to be a veritable dynamo of action, animating the entire project with a vitality never seen in any laboratory. Los Alamos will go down in history as Oppie's greatest poem.

The welding together of long-hairs and short-hairs was given daily demonstrations at Los Alamos. In their cubicles the theoretical scientists would sit for many hours working with pieces of colored chalk on a blackboard or with pencil on pads of paper. At frequent intervals one would hear the boom of great explosions on the various proving grounds in the distant canyons. These were in the true sense explosions of ideas in the minds of men. The mathematical symbols on the blackboards and pads of paper were exploding in the canyons below. Thousands of such ideas exploded simultaneously over Alamogordo, and over Japan.

There were literally hundreds of problems to be solved before the way could be cleared for the fast neutron to do its job unimpeded. One of the principal ones was the accurate determination of the critical mass. Another, of course, was the problem of the efficiency of the explosion. Others involved the proper mechanisms to bring it about. They would have been difficult enough under any circumstances, even under ideal conditions; but here for a long time the men of Los Alamos had to make bricks without straw. Worse still, they were called upon to devise ways for making bricks without clay. They had been assigned to make bombs of U.235 and plutonium when even the ground for the plants to produce these substances had not yet been broken.

Yet by the time these substances became available, a vast amount of groundwork had been laid by the use of substitute materials, and a great deal of information gathered on the habits, behavior, and mode of action of fast neutrons under a variety of conditions. On the basis of these preliminary facts, the theoretical physicists and mathematicians arrived at a much closer approximation of the critical size. As small quantities of the material began trickling in from Oak Ridge and Hanford, they were subjected to tests to check the accuracy of these extrapolations. Step by step experiment was thus correlated with theory, and theory with experiment. By the time enough material was available to make a full-scale model of the bomb, every part had been worked out to the last detail and all that was left to be done was to insert the active material in its proper place.

"Each component did exactly what it was expected to do," Dr. Oppenheimer said to me on the morning after the New Mexico test. Failure of any one of these parts would have meant failure of the whole. On the proper performance of each hung the lives of thousands, or tens of thousands.

That none of the parts failed, however, was no accident. Each one of these was subjected to hundreds of tests. These tests were in themselves marvels of ingenuity and inventiveness. One of them, devised by Dr. Oppenheimer and Dr. Robert Serber, and carried out with special apparatus designed by Professor Bruno Rossi of Cornell, made it possible to get an approximation of the forces that would develop inside an atomic bomb at the instant of explosion, without the use of any U.235 or plutonium. Since the explosion takes place in a fraction of a microsecond, this was more than taking time by the forelock; it meant catching it by the tail.

The test at Alamogordo climaxed a series of other tests the world has not yet heard about, which in their way were equally spectacular and considerably more daring. As soon as sufficient quantities of the active material to form what the calculations indicated would constitute a critical mass became available, tests were begun to check the accuracy of these calculations. In one of these a strange contraption known as the guillotine was rigged up. It consisted of a large wooden frame divided by two parallel vertical steel rods. To each of these rods was attached a large block of the active material. On top between the rods was suspended a smaller block of the substance. The three blocks together formed a critical mass. At a given signal the executioner allowed the smaller block to drop through the space between the two larger ones, the three blocks coming together, thus forming a critical mass for a fraction of a second. The guillotine was hooked up with a series of neutron-counters that registered the neutron flux at the time of criticality.

In another series of experiments a pile containing uranium and a moderator was built. The moderator, of course, made it a slow-neutron chain-reacting pile. Then bit by bit the moderator was removed, thus gradually changing the slow-neutron reaction to a reaction with fast neutrons, approaching more and more closely the conditions prevailing in the bomb.

This model of the atomic bomb was located in one of the semi-underground structures in one of the canyons. The scientists devised a series of extremely sensitive automatic controls that were to stop the reaction if it showed any signs of getting too close to critical. Outside, in the moonlit canyon, six motorcars with their engines running, their drivers tense at the wheels, were ready

186

for a quick getaway. In charge of these tests was Dr. O. R. Frisch, the same Dr. Frisch who, with Dr. Meitner, was the first to demonstrate the fission of uranium.

The controls worked. Dr. Frisch and his small band returned to their homes on the mesa at the break of dawn. They were all set for Alamogordo.

The great cloud of fire that rose more than eight miles to the stratosphere over the New Mexico desert symbolized a funeral pyre for the Japanese Empire. The select few who witnessed the spectacle knew for certain at the instant of the explosion that the new weapon would prove decisive in a relatively short time. No power on earth, everyone realized, could stand up against the elemental force liberated in those bombs.

Ten minutes after the explosion the following dialogue took place between General Farrell and General Groves:

General Farrell: "The war is over!"

General Groves: "Yes, it is over as soon as we drop one or two on Japan!"

The weeks preceding the test, when the scientists were putting the final touches on the gadget, witnessed the most dramatic scenes in the history of scientific endeavor. The decision to make the test had opened up a host of serious problems. A site had to be found far away from inhabited localities. Measures had to be taken to prevent the tremendous thunderbolt, which was expected to be seen and heard for hundreds of miles, from giving away our greatest secret. Apparatus and techniques had to be devised to study, from a distance of several miles, entirely by automatic controls, phenomena that occur in less than a millionth of a second. These included measurements of what takes place inside the atomic bomb at the time of explosion; the amounts and types of energy released; the effect, intensity, and extent of the blast; the post-explosion radiations on the ground and in the air; meteorological observations; and a host of other phenomena that took five typewritten pages to enumerate.

The studies were devised to make the bomb tell its story before, during, and after the detonation. For this purpose scores of the most delicate measuring, photographing, and recording devices, old and new, were placed in concrete pillboxes and underground shelters over a radius of many miles. These included a number of high-speed cameras of all types, numerous electronic devices, supersonic detectors, all sorts of instruments for probing inside the infinitesimal world of the atom's nucleus, devices to measure the intensity of the blast, radiation meters, and a host of other special equipment.

It required about 500 miles of wiring to connect the various electrically operated instruments in the bomb-proof shelters several miles away with the site of the gadget. Seismographs were placed at various distances to measure the effects of the atomic explosion underground, and specially equipped B-29 Superfortresses went aloft to study the effects in the upper atmosphere. More than 300 scientists, including a number of Nobel prize winners, were involved in the test. About 250 military personnel were engaged in carrying out the security and protective measures.

A providential warning that came a few days before the test led to hasty last-minute changes designed to prevent a possible catastrophe that had not been foreseen. A bomb containing ordinary explosives, but otherwise an exact duplicate of the atomic gadget, had been set up on the tower as a practice model. A thunderstorm came along and touched it off. This led to protective measures against the possibility that a bolt of lightning might set off the first atomic explosion on earth, possibly at a time when the scientists were still in its vicinity.

The northwestern section of the 2,000-square-mile Alamogordo Air Base was chosen as the test site because of its remoteness from large towns, isolation, inaccessibility, and desirable meteorological characteristics. The nearest inhabited locality is the village of Carrizozo, population 1,500, about thirty air-line miles due east from the spot selected for the test. Other communities in the locality are Socorro, population 3,500, about thirty miles to the northwest, and Alamogordo, fifty miles to the southeast. The nearest large city is Albuquerque, about 125 miles to the northwest.

Everything relating to the gadget—the spot where it stood on its tower, the time scheduled for its blow-off, as well as the great god It of the occasion—were referred to as Zero, the code name for the test. For everyone concerned, Zero became the center of the universe. Time and space began and ended at Zero. All life centered on Zero. Everyone thought only of Zero and the zero hour, or rather the zero microsecond.

The transfer of the gadget over a distance of more than two hundred miles from Los Alamos to Zero presented a major problem, involving both security and safety. The transportation of this precious stuff, possessing a value inestimable in terms of worldly considerations, was in charge of the Military Intelligence branch at Los Alamos, headed by Captain Thomas O. Jones, formerly a Chicago lawyer.

Several units of the complicated assembly left Los Alamos on Thursday morning, July 12, 1945, in a convoy accompanied by armed guards and several scientists, and arrived at its destination that same afternoon. Another convoy left Los Alamos at 12.01 Friday morning, July 13, arriving at Zero nine hours later. Professors Bacher and

Kistiakowsky were in charge of the assembly of the principal units of the gadget. Tests by the score were carried out to make certain that every part functioned properly. A week earlier a group of leading radiologists under the direction of Colonel Warren had begun setting up a network of radiological stations at various distances to measure the radiation effects of the explosion.

Final assembly of the bomb began on the night of July 12, in an old ranch house. Specialty teams, composed of the top men on specific aspects of science, all of which were bound up in the whole, took over their specialized parts of the assembly. In each group was centralized months and even years of channelized endeavor. As various component assemblies arrived from distant points, tension among the scientists rose to an increasing pitch. Failure was an ever present possibility. They also knew that one false move would blast them and their entire effort into eternity. And a few were also haunted by the specter of too great a success.

Dr. Bacher was the man charged with the assembly of the vital core. A bad few minutes developed when an important section, after insertion, apparently became tightly wedged and would go no farther. Dr. Bacher, however, was undismayed, and reassured the group that time would solve the problem. After three minutes, which seemed an eternity, the entire unit, which had been machine-tooled to the finest measurement, gradually slid down to its place and the basic assembly was completed without further incident.

On Saturday, July 14, the unit was elevated to the top of the steel tower. All that day and the next the job of preparation went on, amid lightning flashes and peals of thunder. In addition to the apparatus necessary to cause the detonation, complete instrumentation to determine the "pulse-beat" and all reactions of the bomb was rigged on the tower.

The last men to inspect the tower with its cosmic bomb were Dr. Bainbridge, Dr. Kistiakowsky and Lieutenant Howard C. Bush, of Brooklyn, N. Y., who was in charge of the Military Police Detachment. These three stood watch on top of the tower from one o'clock until a half hour before zero, their silhouettes outlined at intervals by a flash of lightning. If they thought of the dummy bomb that had been touched off by lightning on the same tower a few days before, they showed no signs of it. They looked very lonely up there, ever so small, yet ever so big, man against the gods.

Before the explosion there had been anxiety on the part of some of those present lest an uncontrollable chain reaction might be started in the atmosphere, though this was contrary to all the known facts about the energies latent in the active substance. One of the younger scientists was so unnerved that, on the advice of the medical men, he was removed from the scene. There is a story current among the physicists that one of the high-ranking military officials, growing more and more tense as he watched the ball of fire expand at a terrific rate, was heard to exclaim: "My God, the long-hairs have lost control!"

Darkening heavens poured forth rain and lightning right up to the zero hour. The weather blocked out aerial observation of the test. Many of Dr. Oppenheimer's assistants were disturbed by the conditions, and some even urged that the test, scheduled for four o'clock, be called off altogether for that night. General Groves and Dr. Oppenheimer kept going out of the control house into the darkness to look at the sky, constantly assuring each other that the one or two visible stars were becoming brighter.

191

"I attempted to shield him," General Groves said, "from the evident concern shown by many of his assistants, who were disturbed by the uncertain weather conditions. By three thirty we decided that we could probably fire at five thirty. By four the rain had stopped, but the sky was heavily overcast. Our decision became firmer as time went on."

Outside Carrizozo a large motorcade of Army trucks and personnel stood waiting. Had the wind suddenly shifted in the direction of that little Spanish-American town, thus threatening to carry the radioactive cloud that way, the men in the motorcade stood ready to dash into every home and carry all the sleeping inhabitants, by force if necessary, to a place of safety. While the blast undoubtedly aroused the sleeping citizens of Carrizozo, they never knew what further surprise would have come their way if there had been a change in the wind.

As the zero hour for the explosion approached, tension in the control room at S-10,000 reached a tremendous pitch. The several observation points in the area were tied in to the control room by radio, and, with twenty minutes to go, Dr. Allison of Chicago University, assistant director at Los Alamos, took over the radio set and made periodic time announcements. The time signals, "minus twenty minutes, minus fifteen minutes," and so on and on, increased the tension to the breaking-point. The last few seconds were described by General Farrell as much worse than any he had experienced during zero hour in the front-line trenches in World War I. Dr. Conant said he had never imagined seconds could be so long.

In a report to the War Department General Farrell gives his impressions of those last long seconds before zero, and the eternal moments that followed:

192

As the time interval grew smaller and changed from minutes to seconds, the tension increased by leaps and bounds. Everyone in that room knew the awful potentialities of the thing that they thought was about to happen. The scientists felt that their figuring must be right and that the bomb had to go off but there was in everyone's mind a strong measure of doubt. The feeling of many could be expressed by "Lord, I believe; help Thou mine unbelief."

We were reaching into the unknown and we did not know what might come of it. It can safely be said that most of those present were praying and praying harder than they had ever prayed before. If the shot were successful, it was a justification of the several years of intensive effort of tens of thousands of people—statesmen, scientists, engineers, manufacturers, soldiers, and many others in every walk of life.

In that brief instant in the remote New Mexico desert, the tremendous effort of the brains and brawn of all these people came suddenly and startlingly to the fullest fruition. Dr. Oppenheimer, upon whom had rested a very heavy burden, grew tenser as the last seconds ticked off. He scarcely breathed. He held on to a post to steady himself. For the last few seconds he stared directly ahead, and then when the announcer shouted "Now!" and there came this tremendous burst of light followed shortly thereafter by the deep growling roar of the explosion, his face relaxed into an expression of tremendous relief. Several of the observers standing back of the shelter to watch the lighting effects were knocked flat by the blast.

The tension in the room let up and all started congratulating each other. Everyone sensed "This is it!" No matter what might happen now all knew that the impossible scientific job had been done. Atomic fission would no longer be hidden in the cloisters of the theoretical physicists' dreams. It was almost full grown at birth. It was a great new force to be used for good or for evil. There was a feeling in that shelter that those concerned with its nativity should dedicate their lives to the mission that it would always be used for good and never for evil.

Dr. Conant reached over and shook hands with General Groves. Dr. Bush, who was on the other side of the General, did likewise. Dr. Kistiakowsky threw his arms around Dr. Oppenheimer and embraced him with shouts of glee. Others were equally enthusiastic. All the pent-up emotions were released in

193

those few minutes and all seemed to sense immediately that the explosion had far exceeded the most optimistic expectations and wildest hopes of the scientists. . . .

As to the present war, there was a feeling that no matter what else might happen, we now had the means to insure its speedy conclusion and save thousands of American lives. As to the future, there had been brought into being something big and something new that would prove to be immeasurably more important than the discovery of electricity or any of the other great discoveries which have so affected our existence.

The effects could well be called unprecedented, magnificent, beautiful, stupendous and terrifying. No man-made phenomenon of such tremendous power had ever occurred before. The lighting effects beggared description. The whole country was lighted by a searching light with the intensity many times that of the midday sun. It was golden, purple, violet, gray and blue. It lighted every peak, crevasse and ridge of the near-by mountain range with a clarity and beauty that cannot be described but must be seen to be imagined. It was that beauty the great poets dream about but describe most poorly and inadequately. Thirty seconds after the explosion, came, first, the air blast, pressing hard against the people and things; to be followed almost immediately by the strong, sustained, awesome roar which warned of doomsday and made us feel that we puny things were blasphemous to dare tamper with the forces heretofore reserved to the Almighty. Words are inadequate tools for the job of acquainting those not present with the physical, mental and psychological effects. It had to be witnessed to be realized.

To Dr. Thomas, of the Monsanto Chemical Company, the cloud "resembled a giant brain the convolutions of which were constantly changing." Only the future will tell whether it symbolized the collective brain that created it or the ultimate explosion of man's collective mind.

The flash lighted up the sky at Albuquerque and was seen as far as Amarillo, Texas, 450 miles east of Zero. At El Paso, 150 miles to the south, persons saw the flash and heard the blast and two successive echoes. Residents of Silver City, New Mexico, 200 miles to the southwest, and at Gallup, New Mexico, 235 miles to the northwest, reported that their windows rattled, and those at Gallup stated that they had also heard two explosions. Various reports from a number of other localities listed the explosion as an earthquake, a meteor, or an airplane crash. Members of the crew and passengers aboard a Santa Fe railroad train near Mountainair, about seventy miles to the northeast, thought they saw a bomber explode and burn in the sky.

The only living beings who dared venture near the spot where Zero vanished in a great cloud of atomic fire were a crew of scientists in two Sherman tanks, the insides of which were lined with lead. In one of these was Dr. Fermi. They took samples of the earth by means of special scoops manipulated from the inside and made preliminary observations of the site, which, later examination revealed, was depressed over a radius of 400 yards to a depth ranging from ten feet at the periphery to twenty-five feet in the center.

A subsequent examination of the ground revealed that all life, vegetable as well as animal, was destroyed within a radius of about a mile. There was not a rattlesnake left in the region, nor a blade of grass. The sand within a radius of four hundred yards was transformed into a glasslike substance the color of green jade. A steel rigging tower weighing thirty-two tons, at a distance of eight hundred yards, was turned into a twisted mass of wreckage. The tower at Zero was completely vaporized. A herd of antelope that had been grazing several miles away had vanished completely. It is believed that they started on a mad dash that ended in the wilds of Mexico. A number of cows at a similar distance developed graying spots on their skins.

CHAPTER FOURTEEN

IN Atomland-on-Mars a man had to go at a pace "twice as fast as he could just to stand still." Events did not occur in sequence, but simultaneously in all places. It had to be taken for granted that things would work as expected, at a time when no one could tell for certain that they would. Instead of taking one step at a time in logical sequence, many steps had to be taken simultaneously all over the map, relying on faith that in the end everything would fit into one grand design.

Hence, long before the test at New Mexico, extensive preparations were made for getting the atomic bomb in action against Japan as soon after the test as possible. This entailed the training of special crews to carry the new weapon to the enemy; the building of modified models of the B-29, specially designed for greater speed, safety, and other requirements; and the preparation of an advance base on Tinian Island, in the Marianas, as a final assembly place for the bomb, since Tinian was at that time (Iwo Jima and Okinawa had not yet been taken) the nearest point of departure for the land of the enemy.

A highly secret base for the training of the special crews was established at the flying field at Wendover, Utah, in the fall of 1944. Here, under Colonel Paul W.

Tibbets, Jr., of Miami, Florida, one of our most distinguished fliers, was organized what later became known as the 509th Composite Group, of the 313th Wing, of the 21st Bombing Command, of the 20th Air Force. He gathered under him seventy-five of the most daring fliers in our Air Force, and an equal number of picked non-commissioned officers and enlisted men, of whom sixty officers and seventy-five non-coms and G.I.'s were to constitute fifteen crews of nine men each, four of whom were officers. In addition, a large ground crew of 1,700 men, all highly skilled in the handling of B-29's, was selected, after a most rigorous screening process, from our far-flung air contingents at home and on the various battlefronts.

With the exception of Colonel Tibbets, no one among the officers or men had the slightest inkling of the nature of their job. All of them had been asked to volunteer for an organization that was "going to do something different." That was all.

They trained through the winter of 1944-5 and the spring of 1945, on the flying field in the bleak Utah desert, in such strict secrecy that their existence was not known even among the top-ranking officers and scientists on the other sites of the Atomic Bomb Project. Since the effectiveness of the bomb was wholly unknown at the time, it was decided from the very beginning not to employ radar, but to drop the bomb visually over the chosen target. Also, it was believed necessary that the bomb be dropped as close to the center of the target as possible. The bombardiers, consequently, had to be chosen for their special ability to drop a bomb right on the button. In Utah they were given further training to enhance this ability.

To simulate combat conditions, and to accustom the fliers to the "something different" they were to carry, an exact model of the atomic bomb (which, by the way, was not yet in existence), made of ordinary explosives but having the same weight and shape, was carried on the training flights and dropped over selected targets in the Utah desert from the same altitude from which the real thing was to be dropped later over Japan. Colonel Tibbets, a perfectionist if there ever was one, trained his men to take off and arrive at a given destination exactly on scheduled time. If a B-29 arrived five minutes late after a long flight, Colonel Tibbets was displeased.

While this was going on in the Utah desert, construction was being rushed on the Atomic Bomb Base on Tinian, under the direction of Oklahoma-born Colonel Elmer E. Kirkpatrick, West Point Class of 1929, one of the ablest construction experts in the Army Corps of Engineers. Tinian was chosen not only because of its proximity to Japan, but also because it lent itself better than Saipan or Guam to the maintenance of strict secrecy.

New Yorkers like myself found themselves at home on Tinian. Its roads and its streets were laid out (doubtless by some homesick Seabee from New York) along the lines of Manhattan Island, with numbered broad avenues running north and south, and numbered crosstown streets east and west. The small atom-town of twenty-one raised tents, where I lived with the atomic bomb scientists during my month's stay at Tinian, was located somewhere in the vicinity of "Times Square." The flying field from which the B-29's took off for Hiroshima and Nagasaki was located somewhere in "upper Manhattan." "Broadway" and "Eighth Avenue" were the two main thoroughfares, along which at all hours of the day and night the atomic bombers rumbled in jeeps and trucks to and from the bomb-assembly area.

As Dr. Morrison described it before the Senate Com-

198

mittee, "Tinian is a miracle." Here, 6,000 miles from San Francisco, the United States armed forces have built the largest airport in the world. A great coral ridge was half-leveled to fill a rough plain, and to build six excellent ten-lane runways, each almost two miles long. Beside these runways stood in long rows the great silvery airplanes, not by the dozen, but by the hundred. From the air this island, smaller than Manhattan, "looked like a giant aircraft carrier, its deck loaded with bombers."

Dr. Morrison's description of what went on every day at Tinian is so graphic that I take the liberty to quote some of it:

> I doubt that there is a more complex and wonderful machine in the world than the B-29. And here at Tinian, far from the factories in Seattle and Wichita, were several hundred of these million-dollar craft. Here were collected tens of thousands of specialists trained in the operation and repair of the delicate mechanisms which cram the body of the plane.
>
> In the harbor every day rode tankers, laden with thousands of tons of aviation gasoline. A net of pipe lines supplied the airfields with fuel. The radio dial was busy with signals of every kind.
>
> And all these gigantic preparations had a grand and terrible outcome. At sunset some day the field would be loud with the roar of the motors. Down the great runways would roll the huge planes, seeming to move slowly because of their size, but far outspeeding the occasional racing jeep. One after another each runway would launch its planes. Once every fifteen seconds another B-29 would become air-borne. For an hour and a half this would continue with precision and order. The sun would go below the sea, and the last planes could still be seen in the distance, with running lights still on.
>
> Often a plane would fail to make the take-off, and go skimming horribly into the sea, or into the beach to burn like a huge torch.
>
> We came often to sit on top of the coral ridge and watch the combat strike of the 313th Wing in real awe. Most of the planes would return the next morning, standing in long single line, like

DAWN OVER ZERO: THE STORY

beads on a chain, from just overhead to the horizon. You could
see ten or twelve planes at a time, spaced a couple of miles
apart. As fast as the near plane would land, another would appear at the edge of the sky. There were always the same number
of planes in sight. The empty field would fill up, and in an hour
or two all the planes would have come in.

This was the environment in which the first atomic
bomb base was set up. It was an island within an island.
The inhabitants of the inner island lived in a world
apart, completely isolated from the other contingents.
In all, including military and civilian personnel, they
numbered fewer than 2,000, of whom 1,850 were avia-
tion personnel. The others included twenty-seven civilian scientists, eleven Navy officers, nine Army officers,
twenty-one enlisted men, all but three of whom were
scientists, and myself.

In an isolated part of the island, far removed from all
other activities and closely guarded by special detach-
ments of M.P.'s, were several Quonset huts transformed
into testing laboratories, and one barricaded, air-conditioned building. Here the small group of scientists from
Los Alamos, under the direction of Professor Norman
F. Ramsey, of Columbia University, assembled the
atomic bomb and prepared it for its final delivery.

The stringent secrecy and the aloofness of the 509th
Group subjected Colonel Tibbets and his crew to considerable ribbing, and life during the months prior to
Hiroshima, already tense, was not made any easier by the
ridicule of fellow fliers, including old comrades on other
battlefields. It was made even more difficult by the fact
that the members of the 509th did not themselves know
what their mission was to be. Every day they would
watch thousands of their comrades take off on missions to
the Empire (as the Japanese main islands were known)
in huge formations, many of them failing to return, many

coming back seriously wounded, whereas all they were doing was to take off now and then in a small formation of three planes, drop a lone missile over enemy territory, and return to base, to face the derision of fliers in other groups. Of course, they did not know at the time that they were making practice runs with simulated atomic bombs over Japan for a dual purpose—to give them further training, and to condition the Japanese to the sight of small formations of B-29's that did comparatively little harm. Then the Japanese, it was reasoned correctly, would pay no attention to the real thing when the time came.

What the other groups on Tinian thought of the 509th was expressed in verse by an anonymous satirist, widely quoted during July and the first days of August. It ran as follows:

> Into the air the secret rose,
> Where they're going, nobody knows.
> Tomorrow they'll return again,
> But we'll never know where they've been.
> Don't ask us about results or such,
> Unless you want to get in Dutch.
> But take it from one who is sure of the score,
> The 509th is winning the war.
>
> When the other Groups are ready to go,
> We have a program of the whole damned show.
> And when Halsey's Fifth shells Nippon's shore,
> Why, shucks, we hear about it the day before.
> And MacArthur and Doolittle give out in advance.
> But with this new bunch we haven't a chance.
> We should have been home a month or more,
> For the 509th is winning the war.

The title of this poem was "Nobody Knows."

To add to their discomfiture, the Japanese radio began poking fun at the 509th.

And so the days, weeks, and months dragged on for Colonel Tibbets's harassed crew. They were no picnic for Colonel Tibbets himself, even though he knew what it was about. For he also knew that everything depended on a certain test in New Mexico, which had not yet taken place. And even if the test were to succeed, that still would not guarantee the success of his first mission, the day for which he knew was drawing close. Success in this case did not mean just "something different." It had to be something revolutionary or it would have to be regarded as a dismal failure.

If before the New Mexico test things had been going at double time, they moved even faster after the event. The Potsdam Conference was then in session, and the first item on the agenda was to inform President Truman of what had taken place. The British Embassy in Washington sent a similar report to Prime Minister Churchill, and it is believed that both informed Premier Stalin.

General Groves and General Farrell sat up nights writing these reports, got a fast little courier plane, and rushed them to Potsdam. These reports, as General Farrell said later, probably "hit the Potsdam conferees with an impact almost equal to that of the bomb itself upon those of us who had the opportunity of seeing it in New Mexico."

It was then decided to get the bomb into combat as rapidly as possible. A large batch of the material was rushed in several planes to San Francisco and loaded on the ill-fated cruiser *Indianapolis*. It arrived in Tinian by the end of July. The last few batches of the active material left the plant on the afternoon of July 26 and were flown to Santa Fe. From there they were taken by truck to Kirtland Field, Albuquerque, where they were picked up by three B-29's of the 509th Group from Wendover and flown to Mather Field at Sacramento, aerial port of embarkation for B-29's, arriving there on the morning of July 28.

Disaster almost overtook one of the three B-29's, named the *Laggin' Dragon* and commanded by Captain Edward M. Costello, West Point Class of 1943, whose home is in Zillah, Washington. Just after he had taken off for Tinian, when the plane was only fifty feet up, the life-raft door blew open and wrapped itself around the right elevator. By that time the B-29 had already crossed the end of the runway and started nosing toward the ground. Captain Costello and his co-pilot, Second Lieutenant Harry B. Davis, started pulling the wheel back with all their strength to raise the elevator, but the big plane kept fluttering so violently that they had all they could do to hold on to the wheel.

They finally managed to raise the whole weight of the raft upward and climbed to three hundred feet. Just then the raft became disengaged and blew off into the air. They signaled the control tower and were advised that if the plane could fly at all, they should remain in the air until their weight was down to 120,000 pounds, when it would be safe to make a landing. The plane at that time weighed 132,000 pounds, one ton heavier than the maximum limit allowed at Mather Field.

Just then they began noticing a flutter in the tail, and the tail gunner, Corporal Maurice J. Clark, reported that large areas of the elevator fabric had been torn away and that more pieces seemed to be tearing off into the wind. Captain Costello therefore notified the tower that he was forced to come in for an emergency landing. There were ten passengers aboard in addition to the crew of nine, and they were all told to get ready for a crash landing.

But as they stood there in crash landing position, hands clasped behind their necks, expecting the worst,

Captain Costello made a perfect landing just when it seemed that the airplane was about to get out of control. The reversible pitch propellers with which the atomic bomb B-29's were equipped had saved the day. It was not even necessary to use the brakes in landing.

Captain Costello did not know what he was carrying, but he had an idea that it must be something precious if three B-29's were required to carry it in three parts all the way to the Marianas. He was determined, he told me, to save the unit at all costs.

The torn elevator was replaced with an elevator taken from a war-weary B-29 that had been on thirty missions, and they took off at 12.30 a.m. on July 30. They arrived at Tinian at 12.15 p.m. August 2, Marianas time. Three days later, on August 5, the bomb was loaded on the *Enola Gay,* Colonel Tibbets's flagship.

The *Indianapolis* was sunk with the loss of nearly all men aboard while on her way to the Philippines, four days after she had delivered her precious cargo to Tinian.

By the end of July General Farrell, deputy to General Groves, arrived to take charge. On his way to Tinian he stopped off at Guam, where he conferred with General Curtis E. LeMay, then in command of the 20th Air Force and about to become the Chief of Staff of the Strategic Forces, and arranged the details of the operation. He then called on Admiral Chester W. Nimitz, whose headquarters were also at Guam, and arranged with him for assistance by the Navy, which included the placing of submarines in Japanese waters along the route the atomic bomb fliers were to take, for the purpose of rescue in case they were forced to bail out or ditch, as well as having in readiness a number of Navy flying boats at near-by bases.

At the end of the conference Admiral Nimitz called

204

General Farrell over to the window and pointed at an island a short distance from Guam.

"That island over there," Admiral Nimitz said, "is Rota. There are about three thousand Japanese on it. They bother us a great deal. They have radios. They know what we are doing. They are sending out information. Haven't you got a small bomb you can drop on Rota? I don't feel it warrants an amphibious invasion at this time. But they do bother us."

"Unfortunately, Admiral," General Farrell replied, "all our bombs are big ones."

Early on the morning of Sunday, August 5, Marianas time (Saturday, August 4, in the United States), there came word that the weather would be favorable for a take-off early next morning. Preparations were at once speeded up to get the bomb ready for immediate loading. But Captain (now Rear Admiral) William S. Parsons, Navy Ordnance expert, who was completely responsible for the technical control of the bomb and for decisions as to its use, was worried. The night before, he had seen four B-29's in a row crash at the end of the runway and burn.

"You know," he said to General Farrell, "if we crack up at the end of the runway tomorrow morning and the plane gets on fire, there is the danger of an atomic explosion and we may lose this end of the island, if not the whole of Tinian with every blessed thing and person on it."

Said General Farrell: "We will just have to pray that it doesn't happen."

"Well," replied Captain Parsons, "if I made the final assembly of that bomb after we left the island, that couldn't happen."

"As I understand it, if that is the way you would work

it, then, if the plane cracks up and burns, we just lose the airplane and the bomb and the crew and you—but we don't lose the island. Is that right?" asked General Farrell.

"Yes," said Captain Parsons.

General Farrell said: "Isn't that nice? Have you ever assembled a bomb like this before?"

"No," said Captain Parsons, "but I've got all day to try it."

"Go ahead and try," said General Farrell.

So Captain Parsons went ahead and began learning the intricacies of the bomb's assembly some hours before take-off time. By afternoon he felt confident that he could do the job. He is a technician of a high order, Admiral Parsons, and a great gentleman.

The bomb, only partly assembled (though to all outward appearances it looked complete), was rolled out of its closely guarded, air-conditioned assembly building and taken to the airfield. By late afternoon it was hanging majestically in the bomb bay of the *Enola Gay,* named by Colonel Tibbets after his mother. It was autographed with all sorts of ribald messages to the Emperor, including one in bold letters from "the boys on the *Indianapolis,*" for whom death had waited just round the corner. There was a lump in every throat and a hope in every heart when the loading job was finally finished.

I arrived in Tinian in the midst of the loading, three days behind schedule. I had been first delayed at Hamilton Field, California, waiting for a transport plane, and then lost another precious day when the C-54 that was taking me to Hickam Field, Hawaii, was forced to turn back after flying half the distance. I was traveling under sealed orders and did not know until I arrived at Guam on the morning of August 5 what my final destination was. At Guam I was met by First Lieutenant Nicholas

Del Genio, of Military Intelligence and Security, who informed me that he was to take me to Tinian.

Though I did not have official knowledge, I had a fairly good notion that I was to be privileged to be an eyewitness of the dropping of the first atomic bomb just as I had witnessed the first test in New Mexico. I became certain of it when, on leaving Washington, I was given an official card bearing the legend: "Valid only if captured by the enemy," and informing the enemy that I was entitled to the privileges of a colonel. As Dr. Alvarez, who carried the same kind of card, said: "I could just see myself coming down in a parachute, waving this card at the natives."

Immediately upon my arrival in Tinian I sought out General Farrell, hoping that there was still time to arrange for my going along. General Farrell, as fine a man as I have ever met, told me it was too late, but that I would go on the next mission, which at that time was scheduled for August 11.

"There may not be any need for another mission," I said. "This one may do the trick."

"I hope you are right," he said.

That same evening at about ten o'clock six selected crews were assembled for briefing. The usual jesting that takes place before a briefing was missing. At last they were about to learn what the something different was for which they had undergone such intensive training and suffered the ridicule of their fellows.

Colonel Tibbets took the platform in the barnlike newly built assembly hall, with its long rows of unpainted wooden benches, and addressed his men as follows:

"Tonight is the night we have all been waiting for. Our long months of training are to be put to the test. We will soon know if we have been successful or failed. Upon our efforts tonight it is possible that history will be made. We are going on a mission to drop a bomb different from any you have ever seen or heard about. This bomb contains a destructive force equivalent to twenty thousand tons of TNT."

He paused, expecting questions. But there was silence in the room, a look of amazement and incredulity on every face.

Colonel Tibbets resumed his talk:

"Because this bomb is so powerful, we must use different tactics from those we have employed when using ordinary bombs."

He then explained the tactics and the part each plane was to play. Three airplanes would take off one hour early, at 1.45 a.m. the next morning. Those planes would act as weather reporters. It was their responsibility to cover three previously selected targets. This would provide the latest weather reports, so that at the proper time the target could be changed should weather conditions make it necessary.

The second three B-29's, one of which was to be the strike plane, to be piloted by Colonel Tibbets, would take off at 2.45 and assemble over Iwo Jima about fifteen minutes after daybreak. This assembly was necessary because the three planes had to enter the target area together.

At midnight there was another briefing, at which all the points were carefully gone over. The men still wore the amazed look of two hours before. They were told what had happened in New Mexico. They were each handed a pair of adjustable arc welders' lenses and warned not to look at the flash with their naked eyes. But what they were being told seemed beyond human comprehension.

That briefing was concluded with a deeply moving

208

prayer by the Chaplain, Captain William B. Downey, of the Hope Lutheran Church at Minneapolis:

"Almighty Father, who wilt hear the prayers of them who love Thee, we pray Thee to be with those who brave the heights of Thy heavens and who carry the battle to our enemies. Guard and protect them, we pray Thee, as they fly their appointed rounds. May they, as well as we, know Thy strength and power, and armed with Thy might may they bring this war to a rapid end. We pray Thee that the end of war may come soon, and that once more we may know peace on earth.

"May the men who fly this night be kept safe in Thy care, and may they be returned safely to us. We shall go forward trusting in Thee, knowing we are in Thy care now and forever. Amen."

Quietly we filed out into the night and proceeded to the mess hall, where Mess Sergeant Elliott L. Easterly, of Lake City, Tennessee, not far from Oak Ridge, served the traditional pre-flight supper.

Here was the menu, with Sergeant Easterly's side remarks:

Look! Real eggs ("How da ya want them?")
Rolled oats ("Why?")
Milk ("No fishing")
Sassage ("We think it's pork")
Apple butter ("Looks like axel grease")
Butter ("Yep, it's out of again")
Coffee ("Saniflush")
Bread ("Someone get a toaster").

After supper we all went to the field and gathered around the *Enola Gay*. Batteries of glaring lights had been set up and hundreds of pictures were taken. There was some danger in that, as there were still many Japs hiding in the hills above the field and they apparently had some way of communicating with the Empire, as on the day the 509th arrived on Tinian, Tokyo Rose welcomed it by name to the theater. The lights and the activities around a single plane might have tipped them off that there was something extraordinary going on.

At exactly 2.45 on Monday morning, August 6, the three B-29's took off from three parallel runways. On the center runway was the *Enola Gay* with Colonel Tibbets at the controls. We waved him good-by and wished him luck. He waved back and smiled, a tired smile.

As soon as the *Enola Gay* started warming up, a few of us entered a jeep and went to the control tower for better observation. We watched Colonel Tibbets hold the *Enola Gay* to the ground almost to the last few feet of the runway. "Will he ever lift her up off the ground?" we wondered. As General Farrell, who was one of the group, said later: "We were almost trying to lift it with our prayers and hopes."

We thought of the four B-29's that had crashed and burned the night before. Those of us who did not know at the time about the conversation between Captain Parsons and General Farrell stood there, frozen.

Then, it seemed almost at the last foot of runway, the *Enola Gay* rose. It soared up into the night, remained visible for a little while, and vanished into the northern sky.

General Farrell and Captain Parsons had a special code for communicating with each other. Each had a copy. Each word in the code meant a full sentence, and the code was considered broad enough to cover any possible situation Parsons might encounter. Parsons assured Farrell he was quite certain that he would be able to destroy that code in case his plane was forced down.

Very few people knew that shortly before he entered

210

the *Enola Gay* Captain Parsons borrowed an automatic pistol from Lieutenant Del Genio. He was the only man aboard who knew all the mysteries of the atomic bomb and he was not going to permit himself to be taken alive.

As soon as the *Enola Gay* and its two companions had taken off, we raced to the communications center, where we could talk with the *Enola Gay* by radiotelephone for about forty-five minutes of travel. During that period General Farrell kept asking Colonel Tibbets how Captain Parsons was getting along with his assembly job. When we lost contact, he was still in the bomb bay working on it.

No one slept that night. For all we knew, Captain Parsons might not have succeeded in putting the bomb together.

211

CHAPTER FIFTEEN

WE spent agonizing hours through the night. There were many burning questions in our minds, coming in the sort of monotonous, repetitious sequence that one sometimes experiences in a nightmare. Did Captain Parsons succeed in assembling the bomb? Would the bomb work? Would it live up to expectations? Would it explode as expected, or would it, God forbid, be a dud, giving our secret away to the enemy? Would our fliers return safely or would they be forced to bail out in enemy waters?

We remembered what happened to the fliers over Tokyo who fell into enemy hands. The lot of Colonel Tibbets's fliers would undoubtedly be even worse. We thought of Captain Parsons and the pistol he had borrowed from Lieutenant Del Genio. We thought of the four scientists in the group—Professor Alvarez and Professor Bernard Waldman of Notre Dame, brilliant young physicists, and their two graduate-student companions, Lawrence H. Johnston, of Hollywood, who spent a lot of his spare time reading the Bible, and Harold Agnew, of the University of Chicago.

It was a night in purgatory, and as daylight came, the hours dragged along on feet of lead. We all knew what a perfectionist Colonel Tibbets was, and the schedule

212

had called for dropping the bomb on Hiroshima, which had been chosen as the primary target, at 9.15, provided the report from the weather plane ahead promised good visibility. If all went well, we were sure, Colonel Tibbets would reach Hiroshima at 9.15, and by 10 o'clock he should be well out of enemy territory, so that Captain Parsons would be able to send General Farrell a message in their code.

And then, exactly at 9.20, came two winged words through the vast distances across the Pacific: "Mission successful!"

On these two words we were transported into the air ourselves. We were flying over Hiroshima, for these two words told us that it was Hiroshima, our primary target, that had been bombed. Those of us who had watched the test in New Mexico could see the great cloud of fire that we knew was just then rising over the ruins of that city. We were flying back with Colonel Tibbets and his gallant crew, at that time still within range of enemy flak or fighter planes.

In the barricaded air-conditioned building work went on as usual on the assembly of the second unit for the next mission, scheduled, as stated, for August 11. But the news somehow made the work go faster.

Only in our little island within the larger island, however, could the great story, which I, as a newspaperman, knew was the world's greatest story, be told. The secret still had to be kept until such time as President Truman announced it to the world, and no one knew when that would be.

The 509th communication center was a busy place that morning. Code messages were sent by General Farrell to General Groves for relay to the President, then still at Potsdam; to Lieutenant General Carl Spaatz, Commander of the Pacific Strategic Air Forces; to Ad-

213

miral Nimitz and General LeMay. Congratulatory messages began coming in a steady stream. In the councils of the mighty, where great decisions were being made, that little island within the tiny island of Tinian became the center of the world.

The news, it is now generally known, hastened Russia's entry into the war against Japan, at a time when President Truman and Prime Minister Attlee were urging Premier Stalin to come in sooner than the Soviet plans then called for. He was still holding out for the original date when President Truman told him the news of Hiroshima. Three days later, just as the second bomb was on its way to Nagasaki, Russia was in the war, and two days after that, Japan offered to surrender.

Among the messages came orders from the Chief of staff, General Marshall, to follow the attack with a great barrage of leaflets over Japan urging the Japanese to surrender if they would avoid total obliteration by an avalanche of atomic bombs. Major John F. Moynahan, of Newark, New Jersey, the Public Relations Officer for the 509th, was a busy man that day, preparing texts for translation into Japanese.

As the *Enola Gay* came nearer to its home base, more detailed messages reached us from Captain Parsons. The news was even better than any of us had dared expect. We knew then that a new day in man's history had been reached; that no matter what happened, the world we lived in would never be the same again.

Colonel Tibbets flashed word that he would land at three o'clock, and we knew that, coming from Colonel Tibbets, the message meant three o'clock, and not five minutes past. So the officers and men of the crews who were to go on the following missions, the only ones who had been told the secret, gathered early at Colonel Tib-

214

bets's hard-stand (the particular spot on an airfield on which a flier parks his plane) to wait for his arrival.

Shortly before three we saw the *Enola Gay* approaching from the north. It was a thing of beauty to behold between the blue Pacific and the clear blue sky, its great silver body shimmering in the sun. We glanced at our watches to time its landing.

It was exactly three o'clock on the afternoon of Monday, August 6, 1945, Marianas time. The first successful atomic bomb mission had come to an end after a round-trip flight of 3,000 miles in an elapsed time of twelve hours and fifteen minutes.

As Colonel Tibbets stepped from the *Enola Gay*, looking even younger than his thirty years, he was greeted by General Spaatz and many other high-ranking officers from Guam and all over the Marianas. In the name of the President, General Spaatz pinned the Distinguished Service Cross, the highest medal that could be given without Congressional authority, on Colonel Tibbets's flying overalls, as his crew stood in line behind him, surrounded by a circle of men who looked upon them as they might on beings who had just arrived from Mars.

The citation read by General Spaatz was in part as follows:

"Flying a B-29 on a daring day strike on Hiroshima, Honshu, carrying for the first time a type of bomb totally new to modern warfare, he successfully dropped his bomb upon reaching the target city," with the result that "tremendous damage was done to the city." This single attack, the citation added, "was the culmination of many months of tireless effort, training and organization unique in AAF history, during which he [Colonel Tibbets] constantly coped with new problems in precision bombing and engineering."

215

Washington and Potsdam were calling frantically for more details, and there was no time lost in getting the fliers to the Quonset that served as the 509th Officers' Club for interrogation. As the fliers were questioned one by one, the story sounded more and more fantastic and awesome, more terrifying than any horror tale in fiction, more like something out of the pages of Dante.

Immediately after the interrogation, at which I took copious notes, I made a beeline for a typewriter. The news, of course, was still top secret, but it was my job to prepare everything I had seen and heard in the form of a news story, give it to Major Moynahan for a preliminary censoring, and then send it to General Groves, who would lock it up in his safe, stamped "Top Secret," to remain there until the news had been officially announced by the President.

I finished my story that same afternoon and it was forwarded that evening to Guam, whence it was to be relayed to Washington. It was no little shock to me, on returning to Washington a month later, to learn that neither that story nor subsequent stories I had written about Hiroshima had ever reached their destination. What happened I do not know to this day.

Since no complete account of the bombing of Hiroshima has ever been published, I herewith reproduce parts of the original lost story, datelined "An Advanced Air Base in the Pacific, Monday, August 6:

The first atomic bomb ever used in warfare, a small, man-made fireball exploding with the force of 20,000 tons of TNT, dropped from a B-29, today wiped out the great Japanese industrial and military center of Hiroshima.

At exactly 9.15 this morning Hiroshima stood out under the clear blue sky. One tenth of a millionth of a

216

second later, a time imperceptible by any clock, it had been swallowed by a cloud of swirling fire as though it had never existed. The best watches made by man still registered 9.15.

If any air-raid wardens below became aware of the approach of the great silver ship high overhead, they gave no sign of it. No flak. No alarm of any kind. The 400,000 inhabitants of Hiroshima, it appeared, were going about their business as usual.

The *Enola Gay* reached the main island of Japan at 8.50 and headed toward its I.P., the initial point of its straight course to the target. It reached this point at 9.11. Major Thomas W. Ferebee, of Mocksville, North Carolina, the bombardier, Captain Theodore J. ("Dutch") Van Kirk, of Northumberland, Pennsylvania, the navigator, and Sergeant Joe A. Stiborik, of Taylor, Texas, the radar operator, here began their final few minutes of co-ordinated teamwork, a job of synchronization fearful and wonderful to contemplate.

The *Enola Gay* had a four-minute run on a perfectly open target. Major Ferebee manipulated the cross hairs in his bomb sight until the target was at the intersection between his course line and his rate line. The great moment had come. He synchronized on Hiroshima and let go.

The great bomb-bay doors of the *Enola Gay* swung open. The inert mass suspended in the interior came to life, freed itself, leaped out. Down toward earth it hurtled until it reached a predetermined point above the ground. There its delicately adjusted mechanisms went into action. Eternal seconds passed.

Those inside the *Enola Gay* first saw a little pin-point of light, purplish red. In an instant the pin-point grew into a giant ball of purple fire, a half mile in diameter. The great fireball suddenly exploded into a huge mass

217

of swirling flames and purple clouds. Out of it came gigantic concentric white rings of fog, as though the earth itself was blowing mighty smoke rings.

The mass seemed to hesitate for a brief instant. Suddenly out of the swirling purple clouds came a huge white column of smoke. Up it went, higher, ever higher, until it reached ten thousand feet.

Then came another phase. The ten-thousand-foot column suddenly grew into a giant mushroom, with tremendous clouds of dust swirling about its base for a distance of three miles. The mushroom kept rising, growing to tremendous heights before the dumfounded eyes of those who watched it from the *Enola Gay* and the other B-29's that followed along as instrument and photographic planes. It kept climbing upward until it reached a height of 45,000 to 50,000 feet, breaking into several layers of a creamy white mass with a purplish tinge, distinguishable from the white clouds through which it penetrated.

Colonel Tibbets, Major Ferebee, and Captain Lewis forgot in the first instant to put on the colored glasses that had been supplied to each member of the crew before departure. They were blinded by the dazzling light of several suns rolled into one. "Everything just turned white in front of me," said Colonel Tibbets. "It felt as though a burst of flak had hit you in the face from a distance of thirty feet."

Along with the flash, one of the two greatest flashes ever seen on earth, came a blast that was heard for hundreds of miles around. It reverberated from the hills surrounding Hiroshima east and west. Both the original blast and the echo hit the *Enola Gay* and made it tremble, though it was several miles away from the scene by the time the blast reached it.

The men in the *Enola Gay* could still see the great

218

column of swirling dust and smoke at a distance of more than four hundred statute miles. "It was solid enough to walk on," one of the crew members said.

Said Captain Robert A. Lewis, co-pilot: "Even when the plane was going in the opposite direction, the flames were still terrific. The area of the town looked as though it was torn apart. I have never seen anything like it— never seen anything like it. When we turned our ship so we could observe results, there in front of our eyes was without a doubt the greatest explosion man had ever seen. The city was nine-tenths covered with a smoke column that in less than three minutes had reached 30,000 feet. We were struck dumb at the sight. It far exceeded all our expectations. Even though we had expected something terrific, what we saw made us feel that we were Buck Rogers twenty-fifth-century warriors. The cloud still kept growing larger even after an hour, when we were some 270 miles away from the target. The pillar of smoke had reached 40,000 feet, 'way above our altitude. It kept changing its weird colors until we lost sight of it."

Here is how Captain Parsons reported it immediately on his return:

"It was a terrific spectacle. The huge dust cloud covered everything. The base of the lower part of the mushroom, a mass of purplish-gray dust about three miles in diameter, was all boiling—the entire area was boiling. A huge white cloud got separated from the top of the mushroom and went upward. Then a second white cloud rose into the air and started chasing the first one. The mushroom top was also boiling, a seething turbulent mass. The mushroom smoke reached our altitude; then another mushroom came up, also very turbulent. There was also another column of smoke off to one side, different in character from the main mass, at a forty-five-degree angle from the ground. It looked as though it was coming from a huge burning fire, and seemed to settle back to earth again. The purple clouds and flames were whirling around. It seemed as though the whole town got pulverized.

"If the Japs say a meteor has hit them, we can tell them we have more where this one came from."

Before the *Enola Gay* took off, I asked Captain Lewis to keep a log of the flight for me and he wrote it in the form of a letter to "Mom and Dad" in Ridgefield Park, New Jersey. Here are some of his entries:

At forty-five minutes out of our base everyone is at work. Colonel Tibbets has been hard at work with the usual tasks that belong to the pilot of a B-29. Captain Van Kirk, navigator, and Sergeant Stiborik, radar operator, are in continuous conversation (on the interphone), as they are shooting bearings on the northern Marianas and making radar wind runs.

At 4.20 Dutch Van Kirk sends me word that we will be at Iwo Jima at 5.25, so we'll just have to check on him to see if he is right.

The Colonel, better known as "Old Bull," shows signs of a tough day, with all he had to do to get this mission off. He is deserving of a few winks, so I'll have a bite to eat and look after "George" (the automatic pilot).

At 4.30 we saw signs of a late moon in the east. I think everyone will feel relieved when we have left our bomb with the Japs and get half way home. Or, better still, all the way home.

The first signs of dawn came to us at 5.00 o'clock, and that also is a nice sight after having spent the previous thirty minutes dodging large cumulus clouds.

It looks at this time (5.51) that we will have clear sailing for a long spell. Tom Ferebee has been very quiet and methinks he is mentally back in the midwest part of old U. S. A.

It is 5.52 and we are only a few miles from Iwo Jima. We are beginning to climb to a new altitude, at which we will remain until we are about one hour away from the Empire.

After leaving Iwo we began to pick up some low strata and before very long we were flying on top of an undercast. At 7.10

the undercast began to break up just a little, but, outside of a high thin cirrus and the low stuff, it is a very beautiful day. We are now about two hours from Bombs Away.

At 7.30 Captain Parsons has put the final touches on his assembly job. We are now loaded. The bomb is now alive. It is a funny feeling knowing it is right in back of you. Knock wood.

We started our second climb to our final altitude at 7.40. Well, folks, it won't be long now.

We have now set the automatic pilot for the last time until Bombs Away. I have checked with all concerned and all stations report satisfactorily.

We have reached proper altitude and at 8.30 Dick Nelson (Radio operator, of Los Angeles, California) received a report from the weather plane (that left an hour ahead of us) that our primary is the best target, so, with everything going well so far, we will make a bomb run on Hiroshima right now, as we are now only twenty-five miles from the Empire, and everyone has a big hopeful look on his face.

It is 8.50. Not long now, folks.

As we are approaching our primary, Ferebee, Van Kirk, and Stiborik are coming into their own, while the Colonel and I are standing by and are giving the boys what they want.

At this point Captain Lewis jotted down: "There will be a short intermission (in the diary) while we bomb our target."

The next entry read:

"My God!"

A reconnaissance mission that flew over Hiroshima five hours after the bombing came back with the report that the city was still hidden under a tremendous cloud of smoke and dust that rose to a height of 45,000 feet. It was not until twenty-eight hours had passed that the first pictures could be taken. They revealed that Hiroshima had been practically wiped off the map in a manner more devastating than if it had been hit by an earthquake of the first magnitude.

Veteran B-29 pilots who had participated in the larg-

221

est raids on Tokyo and other Japanese cities, as well as in the great raids in the final stages of the war in Europe, agreed that nothing even approaching the effects of the atomic bomb had ever been observed by any of them. Experienced reconnaissance fliers who had visited scenes of bombing raids soon after they were made reported that never before had they seen a target so completely hidden by smoke and dust five hours following a raid.

Along with preparations to give the Japanese militarists a second taste of atomic bombing, should they fail to heed the lesson of the first, measures were also taken, as I have said, to inform the Japanese people of what was in store for them unless they petitioned their Emperor to end the war. The following is the text of a leaflet dropped by the millions over Japan:

TO THE JAPANESE PEOPLE

America asks that you take immediate heed of what we say on this leaflet.

We are in possession of the most destructive explosive ever devised by man. A single one of our newly developed atomic bombs is actually the equivalent in explosive power to what 2,000 of our giant B-29's can carry on a single mission. This awful fact is one for you to ponder and we solemnly assure you it is grimly accurate.

We have just begun to use this weapon against your homeland. If you still have any doubt, make inquiry as to what happened to Hiroshima when just one atomic bomb fell on that city.

Before using this bomb to destroy every resource of the military by which they are prolonging this useless war, we ask that you now petition the Emperor to end the war. Our President has outlined for you the thirteen consequences of an honorable surrender. We urge that you accept these consequences and begin the work of building a new, better, and peace-loving Japan.

You should take steps now to cease military resistance. Otherwise, we shall resolutely employ this bomb and all our other superior weapons to promptly and forcefully end the war.

CHAPTER SIXTEEN

I WAS in the barricaded, air-conditioned building, early on the morning of Tuesday, August 7, watching the atomists at work on the assembly of the second atomic bomb, when an excited voice over the shortwaves trumpeted the news that President Truman had announced the dropping of the atomic bomb over Hiroshima. The world's greatest secret had at last been told.

It was a curious sensation to stand there right at the very heart of things, knowing that all the world was just then being electrified, as it were, with the very energy of the substance a few feet away from the radio. Strangely enough, the men who were just then assembling the bomb, who had been in on the secret for a long time, listened with the eagerness of those hearing a startling piece of news for the first time. It was shocking at first to hear terms such as "atomic energy," "uranium 235," "atomic bomb," come out openly on the radio. These words had been strictly taboo. They were never uttered even in a whisper. One always talked about such things in code. There were always animated conversations about "barber shops" and "pigs," or we called numbers, like a quarterback calling signals, or the letters of the alphabet.

For me the broadcast had an added meaning. The

world's greatest story was being broadcast, and mine had been the honor, unique in the history of journalism, of preparing the War Department's official press releases for world-wide distribution. No greater honor could have come to any newspaperman, or anyone else for that matter.

More than ten years ago the editor of a popular periodical circulated a questionnaire among newspapermen asking them to conceive an event in the indefinite future that they would consider "the world's greatest story." My answer was: "The discovery of means for harnessing atomic energy." And here I was, watching an atomic bomb being put together. And the day after tomorrow I was expecting to accompany it to Japan to see it in action.

Being close to it and watching it as it was being fashioned into a living thing, so exquisitely shaped that any sculptor would be proud to have created it, one somehow crossed the borderline between reality and nonreality and felt oneself in the presence of the supranatural. Could it be that this innocent-looking object, so beautifully designed, so safe to handle, could in much less time than it takes to wink an eye annihilate an entire city and its population? Could that comparatively little thing produce the flash of many suns and make the earth tremble for many miles?

Even those who had worked with it for many months never got quite used to the awe and wonder of it. The human mind is simply not conditioned to think in such dimensions. You knew it as a fact because your senses told you so; you could explain it on the basis of the Einstein equation as definitely proved by exact laboratory experiments; but it still remained beyond the grasp of one's comprehension.

This feeling of incredulity was demonstrated some

224

time after the Nagasaki bombing when General Spaatz visited the bomb-assembly building. Dr. Charles P. Baker of Cornell University was showing him and several other high-ranking air officers how the bomb was put together. Among other things he showed them the case in which the active material for the Nagasaki bomb had been carried.

General Spaatz carefully examined the dimensions of the inside of the case. "Of course," he said, "the atoms in the material carried in here served as a fuse that set off the atoms of the air over Nagasaki."

"Oh no, General!" said Dr. Baker, somewhat taken aback, "the explosion came entirely from the material carried in this case."

"Young man," said General Spaatz, "you may believe it. I don't."

The announcement of the news about Hiroshima was indeed welcome to the members of the 509th Group, from Colonel Tibbets down to the ground crews. They had been taking a beating for months about the 509th "winning the war," and it was now their turn. A long poem, entitled "Atomic Might," signed by Sergeant Harry Barnard, was mimeographed and widely circulated. Here are some stanzas as samples:

> It was the 6th of August, that much we knew,
> When the boys took off in the morning dew.
> Feeling nervous, sick and ill at ease
> They flew at the heart of the Japanese,
> With a thunderous blast, a blinding light,
> And the 509th's atomic might.

> From out the air the secret fell
> And created below a scene of hell.
> Never before in time's fast flight
> Has there been displayed such a sight
> As the thunderous blast, the blinding light,
> Of the 509th's atomic might.

From pole to pole, around the earth,
Folks now knew of our powerful worth,
With the thunderous blast, the blinding light,
Of the 509th's atomic might.

The members of the crew of the *Enola Gay* were, of course, paid particular homage. It was interesting to listen to Major Ferebee, the bombardier, answer questions about how he had dropped the bomb. His answer would be: "I dropped it exactly thirteen and a half feet northeast of the aiming point." Or he would say: "Our orders said to bomb the target at 9.15 a.m. I looked at my watch. It was 9.15. I pulled the release. The bomb hit the target. That's all." Major Ferebee had more than fifty missions over Europe to his credit and was reputed to be one of the best bombardiers in the air forces.

As I have already mentioned, our second mission had been planned for August 11, but long-range weather forecasts indicated bad weather conditions beginning on that date that might last for a week or more. It is quite possible, though I have no direct knowledge of it, that the forecast of bad weather came all the way from Potsdam. Be that as it may, the date for the second mission was advanced by two days.

It was not until the evening of Wednesday, August 8, only a few hours before the scheduled take-off, that I was notified by a messenger from General Farrell that I was to go along on that mission as the official reporter. I had almost given up hope, and was in the act of commiserating with a British scientist, Professor William G. Penny, and two others of the American group, who also had expected to go but had had no official word. We must have startled everyone around us by the whoops with which we received the news.

I shall never forget Major Ferebee's kindness on that occasion. When he heard that I was going, he took me

226

to the supply room and saw to it that I was properly equipped with the paraphernalia carried by fliers on a B-29. He lent me his personal survival belt, and showed me how the equipment is used. He went with me to the briefing and from there transported me in his jeep to the flying field, where we all stood around talking of this and that until take-off time.

Before long I found myself sitting on a hard metal box in the cramped quarters of the nose of the B-29. It was 3.30 in the morning, and the night outside was dark and not too promising.

I watched Captain Frederick C. Bock, the pilot of our ship, go through the intricate motions of lifting a B-29 off the ground and marveled at the quiet efficiency of this Michigan boy who had majored in philosophy at Chicago University. I had talked to him on the ground and I was amazed at the transformation that had taken place. Man and machine had become one, a modern centaur. All the nine members of the crew were miraculously synthesized before me into a new entity, of which the machine, with its maze of instruments and mechanical brains, was part of a whole. I soon heard the whir of the propellers and the roar of the four motors. I was in a chariot drawn by the power of eight thousand horses— eight thousand horses with wings.

The second atomic bomb mission to Japan was on its way.

CHAPTER SEVENTEEN

WITH the Atomic Bomb Mission to Japan, Thursday August 9.

We are on our way to bomb the homeland of Japan, in a formation equivalent to 2,000, and possibly 4,000, B-29 Superbombers. Actually our flying contingent consists of only three specially designed B-29's, and two of these carry no bombs. But our lead plane, about 3,000 feet directly ahead, is on its way with another atomic bomb, the second in three days, concentrating in its active substance an explosive energy equivalent to 20,000, and under favorable conditions 40,000, tons of TNT.

We have several chosen targets. One of these is the great industrial and shipping center of Nagasaki, on the western shore of Kyushu, one of the main islands of the Japanese homeland. But we shall not know for certain until about half an hour before bombs-away which one of these will be the actual target. That will depend on the weather reports to be sent to us on conditions over the military and industrial centers selected for the second atomic bombing.

I watched the assembly of this man-made meteor during the past two days, and was among the small group of scientists and Army and Navy representatives present at

228

the ritual of its loading in the Superfort last night, against a background of threatening black skies torn open at intervals by great flashes of lightning.

This atomic bomb is different from the bomb used three days ago with such devastating results on Hiroshima.

I saw the atomic substance before it was placed inside the bomb. By itself it is not at all dangerous to handle. It is only under certain conditions, produced in the bomb assembly, that it can be made to yield up its energy, and even then it gives up only a small fraction of its total contents—a fraction, however, large enough to produce the greatest explosion on earth.

The briefing at midnight revealed the extreme care and the tremendous amount of preparation that had gone into every detail of the mission, to make certain that the atomic bomb fully served the purpose for which it was intended. Each target in turn was shown on detailed maps and in aerial photographs. Every detail of the course was rehearsed—navigation, altitude, weather, where to land in emergencies. It transpired that the Navy had submarines and rescue craft, known as Dumbos and Superdumbos, stationed at various strategic points in the vicinity of the targets, ready to rescue the fliers if they were forced to bail out.

The briefing period ended with another moving prayer by Chaplain Downey:

Almighty God, Father of all mercies, we pray Thee to be gracious with those who fly this night. Guard and protect those of us who venture out into the darkness of Thy heaven. Uphold them on Thy wings. Keep them safe both in body and soul and bring them back to us. Give to us all courage and strength for the hours that are ahead; give to them rewards according to their efforts. Above all else, our Father, bring peace to Thy world. May we go forward trusting in Thee and knowing we are in Thy presence now and forever. Amen.

229

We then proceeded to the mess hall for the traditional early morning breakfast before departure on a bombing mission. For many a brave lad this was the last breakfast.

A convoy of trucks took us to the supply building for the special equipment carried on combat missions. This included the Mae West, a parachute, a lifeboat, an oxygen mask, a flak suit, and a survival vest. We still had a few hours before take-off time, but we all went to the flying field and stood around in little groups or sat in jeeps, talking rather casually about our mission.

In command is Major Charles W. Sweeney, of North Quincy, Massachusetts. His flagship, carrying the atomic bomb, is named the *Great Artiste,* but the name does not appear on the body of the great silver ship, with its unusually long, four-bladed, orange-tipped propellers. Instead it carries the number 77, and someone remarks that it was Red Grange's winning number on the gridiron.

The co-pilot of our strike ship is First Lieutenant Charles D. Albury, of Miami, Florida. The bombardier, upon whose shoulders rests the responsibility of depositing the atomic bomb square on its target, is Captain Kermit K. Beahan, of Houston, Texas, who is celebrating his twenty-seventh birthday today. The navigator is Captain James F. Pelt, Jr., of Oak Hill, West Virginia. The lead ship is also carrying Commander Frederick L. Ashworth of the Navy, the "weaponeer," and Lieutenant Jacob Beeser, of Baltimore, an expert on air-borne radar.

The other two Superfortresses in our formation are instrument planes, carrying special apparatus for measuring the power of the bomb at the time of explosion, high-speed cameras, and other photographic equipment.

Our Superfort is second in line. In addition to Captain Bock, who comes from Greenville, Michigan, its officer personnel are Second Lieutenant Hugh C. Ferguson, of Highland Park, Michigan, pilot; Second Lieutenant

230

Leonard A. Godfrey, of Greenfield, Massachusetts, navigator; and First Lieutenant Charles Levy, of Philadelphia, bombardier.

On the third B-29, commanded by Major James Hopkins, of Palestine, Texas, are two distinguished observers from Britain, whose scientists were important in the development of the atomic bomb. One of these is Group Captain G. Leonard Cheshire, famous Royal Air Force pilot, a member of the British Military Mission to the United States. The other is Dr. Penny, professor of applied mathematics at London University, one of the group of eminent British scientists at Los Alamos. Group Captain Cheshire, whose rank is equivalent to that of colonel in the United States Army Air Forces, was designated as an observer of the atomic bomb in action by Winston Churchill when he was still Prime Minister of Britain. He is now the official representative of Prime Minister Attlee.

We took off at 3.50 this morning and headed northwest on a straight line for the Empire. The night was cloudy and threatening, with only a few stars here and there breaking through the overcast. The weather report had predicted storms ahead part of the way, but clear sailing for the final and climactic stages. We were about an hour away from our base when the storm broke. Our great ship took some heavy dips through the abysmal darkness around us, but it took these dips much more gracefully than a large commercial airliner, producing a sensation more like a glide than a bump, like a great ocean liner riding the waves, except that the air waves were much higher and the rhythmic tempo of the glide much faster.

I noticed a strange eerie light coming through the window high above the navigator's cabin, and as I peered through the dark all around us, I saw a startling phenomenon. The whirling giant propellers had somehow become great luminous disks of blue flame. The same luminous blue flame appeared on the plexiglass windows in the nose of the ship and on the tips of the giant wings. It looked as though we were riding the whirlwind through space in a chariot of blue fire.

It was, I surmised, a surcharge of static electricity that had accumulated on the tips of the propellers and on the dielectric material in the plastic windows. My thoughts dwelt anxiously on the precious cargo in the invisible ship ahead of us. Was there any danger that this heavy electric tension in the atmosphere all about us might set it off?

I expressed my fears to Captain Bock, who seemed nonchalant and unperturbed at the controls. He quickly reassured me. "It is a familiar phenomenon seen often on ships. I have seen it many times on bombing missions. It is known as St. Elmo's fire."

On we went through the night. We soon rode out the storm and our ship was once again sailing on a smooth course straight ahead, on a direct line to the Empire.

Our altimeter showed that we were traveling through space at a height of 17,000 feet. The thermometer registered an outside temperature of 33 degrees below zero Centigrade, about 30 below Fahrenheit. Inside our pressurized cabin the temperature was that of a comfortable air-conditioned room, the pressure corresponding to an altitude of 8,000 feet. Captain Bock cautioned me, however, to keep my oxygen mask handy in case of emergency. This, he explained, might mean either something going wrong with the pressure equipment inside the ship or a hole made through the cabin by flak.

The first signs of dawn came shortly after five o'clock. Sergeant Ralph D. Curry, of Hoopeston, Illinois, who had been listening steadily on his earphones for radio reports while maintaining a strict radio silence himself, greeted it by rising to his feet and gazing out the window.

"It's good to see the day," he told me, "I get a feeling of claustrophobia hemmed in in this cabin at night."

He is a typical American youth, looking even younger than his twenty years. It takes no mind-reader to read his thoughts.

"It's a long way from Hoopeston," I found myself remarking.

"Yep," he replied as he busied himself decoding a message from outer space. "Think this atomic bomb will end the war?" he asked hopefully.

"There is a very good chance that this one may do the trick," I assured him, "but if not, then the next one or two surely will. Its power is such that no nation can stand up against it very long."

This is not my own view. I had heard it expressed all around a few hours earlier, before we took off. To anyone who has seen this man-made fireball in action, as I had less than a month ago in the New Mexico desert, this view did not seem overoptimistic.

By 5.50 it is light outside. We have lost our lead ship, but Lieutenant Godfrey, our navigator, informs me that we have arranged for that contingency. We have an assembly point in the sky above the little island of Yakoshima, southeast of Kyushu, at 9.10. We are to circle there and wait for the rest of our formation.

Our genial bombardier, Lieutenant Levy, comes over to invite me to take his front-row seat in the transparent nose of the ship and I accept eagerly. From that vantage point in space, 17,000 feet above the Pacific, one gets a view of hundreds of miles on all sides, horizontally and vertically. At that height the vast ocean below and the sky above seem to merge into one great sphere.

233

I am on the inside of that firmament, riding above the giant mountains of white cumulus clouds, letting myself be suspended in infinite space. One hears the whir of the motors behind one, but it soon becomes insignificant against the immensity all around and is before long swallowed by it. There comes a point where space also swallows time and one lives through eternal moments filled with an oppressive loneliness, as though all life had suddenly vanished from the earth and you are the only one left, a lone survivor traveling endlessly through interplanetary space.

My mind soon returns to the mission I am on. Somewhere beyond these vast mountains of white clouds ahead of me lies Japan, the land of our enemy. In about four hours from now one of its cities, making weapons of war for use against us, will be wiped off the map by the greatest weapon ever made by man. In a fraction of time immeasurable by any clock a whirlwind from the skies will pulverize thousands of its buildings and tens of thousands of its inhabitants. But at this moment no one yet knows which one of the several cities chosen as targets is to be annihilated. The final choice lies with destiny. The winds over Japan will make the decision. If they carry heavy clouds over our primary target, that city will be saved, at least for the time being. None of its inhabitants will ever know that the wind of a benevolent destiny had passed over their heads. But that same wind will doom another city. Our weather planes ahead of us are on their way to find out where the wind blows. Half an hour before target time we shall know what the winds have decided.

Does one feel any pity or compassion for the poor devils about to die? Not when one thinks of Pearl Harbor and of the Death March on Bataan.

Captain Bock informs me that we are about to start

234

our climb to bombing altitude. He manipulates a few knobs on his control panel to the right of him and I alternately watch the white clouds and ocean below me and the altimeter on the bombardier's panel.

We reached our altitude at nine o'clock. We were then over Japanese waters, close to their mainland. Lieutenant Godfrey motioned to me to look through his radarscope. Before me was the outline of our assembly point. We shall soon meet our strike ship and proceed on the final stage of our journey.

We reached Yakoshima at 9.12 and there, about 4,000 feet ahead of us, was the *Great Artiste* with its precious load. I saw Lieutenant Godfrey and Sergeant Curry strap on their parachutes, and I decided to do likewise.

We started circling. The little towns on the coastline were heedless of our presence. We kept on circling, waiting for the third ship in our formation.

It was 9.56 when we began heading for the coastline. The code messages sent us by our weather scouts and deciphered by Sergeant Curry informed us that both the primary and the secondary targets were clearly visible. The winds of destiny seemed to favor certain Japanese cities that must remain nameless. We circled about them again and again and found no opening in the thick umbrella of clouds that covered them. Destiny chose Nagasaki as the ultimate target.

We had been circling for some time when we noticed black puffs of smoke coming through the white clouds directly at us. There were fifteen bursts of flak in rapid succession, all too low. Captain Bock changed his course. There soon followed eight more bursts of flak, right up to our altitude, but this time they were too far to the left.

We flew southward down the channel and at 11.33 crossed the coastline and headed straight for Nagasaki about one hundred miles to the west. Here again we circled until we found an opening in the clouds. It was 12.01, and the goal of our mission had arrived.

We heard the prearranged signal on our radio, put on our arc welders' glasses, and watched tensely the maneuverings of the strike ship about half a mile in front of us.

"There she goes!" someone said.

Out of the belly of the *Great Artiste* what looked like a black object went downward.

Captain Bock swung around to get out of range; but even though we were turning away in the opposite direction, and despite the fact that it was broad daylight in our cabin, all of us became aware of a giant flash that broke through the dark barrier of our arc welders' lenses and flooded our cabin with intense light.

After the first flash we removed our glasses, but the light lingered on, a bluish-green light that illuminated the entire sky all around. A tremendous blast wave struck our ship and made it tremble from nose to tail. This was followed by four more blasts in rapid succession, each resounding like the boom of cannon hitting our plane from all directions.

Observers in the tail of our ship saw a giant ball of fire rise as though from the bowels of the earth, belching forth enormous white smoke rings. Next they saw a giant pillar of purple fire, 10,000 feet high, shooting skyward with enormous speed.

By the time our ship had made another turn in the direction of the atomic explosion the pillar of purple fire had reached the level of our altitude. Only about forty-five seconds had passed. Awe-struck, we watched it shoot upward like a meteor coming from the earth instead of from outer space, becoming ever more alive as it climbed skyward through the white clouds. It was no longer smoke, or dust, or even a cloud of fire. It was a living

236

thing, a new species of being, born right before our incredulous eyes.

At one stage of its evolution, covering millions of years in terms of seconds, the entity assumed the form of a giant square totem pole, with its base about three miles long, tapering off to about a mile at the top. Its bottom was brown, its center amber, its top white. But it was a living totem pole, carved with many grotesque masks grimacing at the earth.

Then, just when it appeared as though the thing had settled down into a state of permanence, there came shooting out of the top a giant mushroom that increased the height of the pillar to a total of 45,000 feet. The mushroom top was even more alive than the pillar, seething and boiling in a white fury of creamy foam, sizzling upward and then descending earthward, a thousand geysers rolled into one. It kept struggling in an elemental fury, like a creature in the act of breaking the bonds that held it down. In a few seconds it had freed itself from its gigantic stem and floated upward with tremendous speed, its momentum carrying it into the stratosphere to a height of about 60,000 feet.

But at that instant another mushroom, smaller in size than the first one, began emerging out of the pillar. It was as though the decapitated monster was growing a new head.

As the first mushroom floated off into the blue it changed its shape into a flowerlike form, its giant petals curving downward, creamy white outside, rose-colored inside. It still retained that shape when we last gazed at it from a distance of about two hundred miles. The boiling pillar of many colors could also be seen at that distance, a giant mountain of jumbled rainbows, in travail. Much living substance had gone into those rainbows.

The quivering top of the pillar was protruding to a great height through the white clouds, giving the appearance of a monstrous prehistoric creature with a ruff around its neck, a fleecy ruff extending in all directions, as far as the eye could see.

We are now on our way to Okinawa to refuel. Our fuel supply is quite low, but with good luck we should have enough to get us there. We are much concerned, however, about No. 77, the *Great Artiste*. As the carrier of the bomb, it started with less fuel than we did. We are praying that its gallant men have not been forced down, and that they did not fall into the hands of the enemy.

It has certainly been a nip-and-tuck affair all the way and we are far from being out of the woods yet. From the time we reached Yakoshima, fate started playing a grim game with us, a fantastic Mephisthophelean chess game. There was at least one occasion on this journey when I said to myself: "Well, old fellow, this may be the last story you'll ever cover," and then, to my own surprise, I found myself unperturbed by the thought. If this was to be my last, could anyone wish for a better?

Our troubles at Yakoshima started when the third plane in our group, which was to make the official photographs of the bombing, did not join us within the expected time limit. We circled and circled, endlessly it seemed, around the little island. More than forty-five minutes had passed when our lead ship decided not to wait any longer.

The weather planes, half an hour ahead of us, had signaled good visibility over the primary as well as the secondary target. But here a malevolent destiny had contrived to delay our arrival over that city by more than three quarters of an hour. When we got there the weather had changed and thick clouds covered the target. We had located the city by radar, but the orders were to make only a visual drop, which has the advantage of greater accuracy. This meant circling until we found an opening through the clouds over the selected target area.

Round and round in wide circles went the *Great Artiste*. Round and round went our ship close behind. But the city remained hidden from our view. All we needed was a small peephole through the white curtain stretching for miles below us, but the curtain remained impenetrable. Vapor was matched against man's mightiest weapon.

Since what was at stake was the ending of the war as quickly as possible, turning back for another try the following morning might mean prolonging the war by at least one day, and every day the war went on meant the loss of many lives. And too much time had passed since the weather plane's report on the visibility over the secondary target. The chances were therefore about even that it was by then no better than over the primary. The dogged determination with which the lead plane kept circling over the latter indicated a decision that it was wiser under the circumstances to continue to look for an opening over the better of the two targets.

This, of course, could go on only until a certain level of the fuel supply was reached. If at that point no opening came, we would have to try our luck with the secondary target.

It was while we were still circling over the primary that the Japs opened fire. They seemed to be aiming at us rather than at the lead plane. Several bursts came pretty close. By that time we were making our third run over the target and had flown over the Empire for about two hours.

Just after we had got out of the range of the flak, we noticed a squadron of twenty-one Jap fighter planes emerging from the clouds, spiraling upward toward us. Thinking of these Jap fighter planes in retrospect, they seem more dangerous than they did during those moments when they were actually threatening us. Death seems to recede in time the closer one comes to it in space. Conversely, it seems to recede in space the closer one comes to it in time. That is why, as one grows older, one gradually learns to accept the fact of approaching death with equanimity.

We had surmised that a shortage of gasoline and the approach of the Jap fighter planes had led Major Sweeney and Commander Ashworth to proceed to the secondary target. A careful check of our fuel supply indicated that Major Sweeney had only enough gasoline for one run on the target, and that if the bomb was not dropped, thus lightening the load, there would not be enough fuel left to take him back to Okinawa, which was to be used as the emergency landing field.

We soon lost sight of the fighters. Either their range was short, or they turned back because they believed they had accomplished their mission by chasing us off an important military target. Since we had been circling over that city for a long time without dropping any bombs, and since our formation consisted of only two planes, they may have believed that our mission was merely for reconnaissance. The lesson of Hiroshima had apparently not yet sunk in.

On we went to Nagasaki, a prayer in everyone's heart for a change in luck. Our radar soon told us that we were approaching the city, and the nearer we came, the greater grew our dejection. Our nemesis had got there ahead of us. Nagasaki, too, was hidden under a curtain of clouds.

Would we drop the bomb by radar if we could not

find an opening on the first and only possible run, and thus risk being 'way off the mark, or would we continue looking for an opening until we had only enough gas left to reach our naval rescue craft in Japanese waters? Maybe we would go even farther—keep on looking for an opening until the last drop and then bail out over enemy territory. What were the misfortunes, or lives, of a handful of men in two B-29's against the chance of shortening the war by several days?

Like my friend Luiz Alvarez, I had an AGO (Adjutant General's Office) card on my person specifying that it was "valid only if captured by the enemy," and informing the enemy that I was entitled to the privileges of a colonel. I said to myself: "Any minute now you may become a colonel!"

It was up to Major Sweeney and Commander Ashworth to make the decision, and they would have to make it fast. I could almost hear them discussing the matter quietly at that very moment. In that plane ahead of us two brave men were just then weighing our fate, and their own, in the balance. And knowing that they were men of stout heart and resolute courage, I felt I knew what their decision would be.

We were then approaching the end of the first run. In a few minutes we would know the answer. The clouds below were still as impenetrable as ever. And then, at the very last minute, there came an opening. For a few brief moments the city of Nagasaki stood out clearly in broad noontime daylight. They were Nagasaki's last brief moments under the sun.

Our watches stood at noon. The seconds ticked away. One, two, three. Ten, twenty, thirty, forty. Fifty. Fifty-seven, fifty-eight, fifty-nine—

It was 12.01 over Nagasaki.

After we had circled the area that a little while before

241

had been the site of the city of Nagasaki, we headed
south for Okinawa, carefully husbanding our precious
fuel. When we reached the coast we had flown over the
Empire for fully three hours and seventeen minutes,
longer by far than any other mission over the land of the
enemy.

We landed in Okinawa this afternoon, our tanks
nearly empty, and there, to our great relief, was No. 77.
On landing, two of its motors stopped dead halfway
down the runway for lack of fuel. When approaching
Okinawa, Major Sweeney had signaled that he was coming in for an emergency landing without circling the
field. To get immediate clearance he sent down the
proper flare, which, however, failed to work. So his crew
shot off all the flares in the B-29 vocabulary, including
the one signifying "wounded aboard." They were met by
all the emergency paraphernalia and personnel on the
field—ambulances, crash wagons, doctors, Red Cross
workers, and priests.

While we were refueling we learned that Russia had
this day entered the war against Japan.

We landed at our base camp at 10.25 tonight and
found that General Farrell, Colonel Tibbets, and their
staffs had been sweating it out on our account for many
anxious hours. Whereas they had received first word
from the Hiroshima mission five minutes after it was
due, hours had gone by without hearing a word from us.
In fact, the first message they had received was from the
photographic plane, which had lost us. It wanted to
know whether No .77 had "aborted," meaning whether
it had been forced down. "We could only pray," General
Farrell said, "that if it had aborted, it had dropped into
the ocean rather than on Japan. We didn't feel our people
were particularly welcome in Japan at that time."

They went to luncheon (General Farrell promptly lost

his), then returned to the communications center and sweated it out some more. Time dragged on. Then shortly after noon they heard the instruments click and the words of the operator:

"Stand by for a message from No. 77!"

CHAPTER EIGHTEEN

WHEN the atomic bombs exploded over Hiroshima and Nagasaki it was as though a flaming fragment from the bowels of one of the hottest stars, three times hotter than the temperature at the center of the sun, had landed on the earth.

At the instant of the explosion, forces of superterrestrial magnitude, fire, blast, pressure, wind, radiant energy, spread death and devastation for miles around. The blast, equal to that of the explosion of more than 20,000 tons of TNT, pushes the air in front of it, creating pressures greater than any ever experienced on earth. The pressure wave is followed by great winds blowing at five hundred to a thousand miles per hour, five to ten times more violent than a hurricane. The radiant energy, similar in kind to X-rays or the gamma rays from radium, is liberated in such quantities at the moment of the explosion that no life can stand up against it within a region of several thousand feet.

In addition to these rays, which are quickly absorbed in the environment and lose their effect, there is also liberated a tremendous quantity of radioactive substances, the fission products of U.235 or plutonium, which in the maximum case are equivalent to thousands of tons of radium. If the bomb is exploded close to the ground, as

244

was not the case in Japan, these "tons of radium," deposited over a large area, may make it uninhabitable for a long time.

The Reverend John B. Siemes, S.J., thirty-nine-year-old German-born Jesuit priest, had come to Hiroshima from ruined Tokyo, where he had served as professor of modern philosophy at Catholic University. That Monday morning in August he sat by the window in his room at the Novitiate of the Society of Jesus, from which he had a clear view down the valley to the edge of the city, about three miles away. He tells what he saw in *Jesuit Missions*.

It was a bright, clear summer morning. An air-raid alarm had sounded about seven o'clock, no doubt provoked by the weather-scouting planes that preceded the *Enola Gay*. The all-clear came at eight. Suddenly, at about 8.14, Hiroshima time, the whole valley was filled by a garish light, while at the same time Father Siemes became conscious of a wave of heat.

As he made for the door, he heard a moderately loud explosion. The window broke in with a loud crash and he was sprayed with fragments of glass. The entire window frame had been forced into the room, and he was bleeding from cuts about the hands and head. He was under the impression that a bomb had burst directly overhead. He forced an opening in the jammed door by repeated blows with his hands and feet and came to the broad hallway, from which opened the various rooms. All windows were broken and all doors forced inwards. He found most of his colleagues injured by fragments of glass.

Down in the valley, at a distance of about one kilometer from the novitiate, or five eighths of a mile, several peasant homes were on fire, and the woods on the opposite side of the valley were aflame. Over the city clouds of smoke were rising. A procession of people began to stream up the valley from the city. "The crowd thickens. Their steps are dragging, their faces blackened. Many are bleeding or have suffered burns." Father Siemes and his colleagues gave them first aid and brought them into the chapel.

About four o'clock in the afternoon came a report that the parish church, the parish house, and adjoining buildings in the center of the city had burned down, that Father Superior Lassalle and Father Schiffer had been seriously injured, and that they had taken refuge in Asano Park on the river bank. Father Siemes and his colleagues hurriedly got together two stretchers and rushed toward the city.

The closer they got, the greater was the evidence of destruction. Houses on the outskirts were all severely damaged. Farther in they found all dwellings consumed by fire. They made their way to the street on the river bank and twice were forced into the river itself by the heat and smoke. All along they met people frightfully burned. By the wayside were many dead and dying. On the Misasi Bridge they met a procession of soldiers who had suffered burns. Abandoned on the bridge, a number of horses with large burns on their flanks stood with sunken heads.

They finally reached the entrance to the park. Even the trees were on fire in several places. A large portion of the populace had taken refuge there. Fallen trees made the paths and bridges almost impassable. At a far corner in the park they at last came upon their injured colleagues. It was now quite dark. Father Schiffer was lying on the ground deadly pale. He had a deep cut behind his ear and had lost so much blood that they feared for his life. Father Lassalle had suffered a deep wound in his leg.

They were in their rooms in the parish house, they told

Father Siemes and the others, when came the intense light and immediately afterward the sound of breaking windows, walls, and furniture. The church and all buildings in the vicinity collapsed at once. Soon fires that had begun some distance away were raging ever closer. It was high time to flee. The secretary of the mission, Mr. Fuaki, was completely out of his mind. He refused to leave the house, explaining that he did not want to survive the destruction of his fatherland. Completely uninjured, he was carried away by force. By that time the way they had meant to flee was no longer open and so they made their way to Asano Park. Fuaki refused to go farther and remained behind. He had not been heard from since.

The transportation of their wounded was difficult. Were they to be carried on the shaky litters in the dark, they would suffer unbearable pain and lose dangerously large quantities of blood. A Japanese Protestant pastor came to the rescue. He had brought along a boat and offered to take the wounded upstream to a place where progress was easier.

They landed on a sandspit that jutted out from the shore. It was covered with wounded, screaming for aid, for they were afraid of drowning when the river rose with the incoming tide. However, Father Siemes records, they had to press on.

A group of soldiers came along the road and their officer noticed that the priests were speaking a foreign language. He at once drew his sword, screamed at them, and threatened to cut them down. Father Laures, Jr., seized his arm and explained that they were German. The officer had believed that they might well be Americans who had parachuted down, as many rumors of parachutes were being circulated about the city.

It had become midnight. They determined to remove

Father Schiffer first to the outskirts of the city. Despite all precautions their progress was stumbling. One of the bearers fell, carrying the litter with him. Father Schiffer became unconscious from the fall and vomited. At the outskirts of the city they put down the litter and turned back to fetch the Father Superior. Most of the ruins were by now burned out. The pungent smell, one of them remarked, reminded him of burned corpses. They finally arrived at the novitiate about half past four. It had taken them almost twelve hours, whereas normally one could go to the city and back in two hours.

Father Siemes got two hours' sleep on the floor. It was now the 7th of August, the anniversary of the restitution of the Society of Jesus. He said a Mass *in gratiarum actionem* and they took off again.

The bright day now revealed the frightful picture that had been partly concealed by the darkness the night before. Where the city had stood, everything, as far as the eye could reach, was a waste of ashes and ruin. The banks of the river were covered with dead and wounded. The rising waters had already covered some of the corpses. Naked burned cadavers were particularly numerous. Among them were wounded still alive. A few had crawled under burned-out autos and trolley cars.

They made their way to the spot where their church had stood. In the ashes they found a few molten remnants of the holy vessels.

They took under their care fifty refugees. The Father Rector treated the wounded as well as he could, but he had to confine himself in general to cleansing the wounds of purulent matter. Even those with smaller burns were very weak, and all suffered from diarrhea. In the eyes of the people, this work, Father Siemes states, "was a greater boost for Christianity than all our work during the preceding long years."

248

During the next few days funeral processions passed the novitiate from morning to night, bringing the dead to a small valley near by, where they were burned. People brought their own wood and cremated the bodies themselves. Late at night the little valley was lit by the funeral pyres.

The magnitude of the disaster that befell Hiroshima [Father Siemes continues] was only slowly pieced together in my mind. As a result of the explosion, almost the entire city was destroyed at a single blow. The small Japanese houses in a diameter of five kilometers [about three miles] collapsed or were blown away. Those in the houses were buried in the ruins. Those in the open sustained burns. Fires spread rapidly. The heat which rose from the ground created a whirlwind which spread the fire throughout the whole city. As much as six kilometers from the center of the explosion all houses were damaged, and many collapsed and caught fire.

Hiroshima had a total population of 400,000. Official statistics place the number who died at 70,000 up to September 1, not counting the missing, and the 130,000 wounded, among them 43,500 severely wounded. Estimates made by ourselves on the basis of groups known to us show that the number of 100,000 dead is not too high.

In February 1946, Supreme Allied Headquarters announced that the casualties in Hiroshima as the result of the atomic bomb were: dead, 78,150; still missing, 13,983; seriously wounded, 9,428; slightly injured, 27,997.

Thousands of the wounded who died later [Father Siemes writes] "could doubtless have been rescued had they received proper treatment and care, but rescue work in a catastrophe of this magnitude had not been envisaged. Since the whole city had been knocked out at a blow, everything prepared for emergency work was lost, and no preparation had been made for rescue work in the outlying districts. Many of the wounded also died because they had weakened by undernourishment and consequently lacked the strength to recover. Those who had their normal strength and received good care slowly healed of their burns.

It was also noised about that the ruins of the city emitted deadly rays, that many workers who went to aid in the clearing died, and that the central district would be uninhabitable for some time to come. I have my doubts as to whether such talk is true. There were cases, however, whose prognosis seemed good where death supervened suddenly. Some who had only small external wounds died within a week or later, after an inflammation of the pharynx and oral cavity. There cannot be any doubt that the bomb's radiation had some effect on the blood. However, myself and others who worked in the ruined area for some hours shortly after the explosion suffered no ill effects.

Only about one person in every house or two within a thousand yards from the blast escaped death from blast or burn. Many crawled out of the wreck of their homes uninjured, but they died from the effect of the radiations emitted at the instant of the explosion (as distinguished from the radiations from the fission products, which were negligible in the Japanese cities because the bomb was detonated at a considerable distance from the ground).

The day before the bomb was dropped, 40,000 people came into Hiroshima to evacuate it. They had started work at seven that morning. All of them were killed by the bomb. Of three hundred registered physicians, more than 260 were unable to aid the injured. Of 2,400 nurses, orderlies, and trained first-aid workers, more than 1,800 were made casualties in a single instant. Twenty-six of the thirty-three modern fire stations in Hiroshima were made useless and three quarters of the firemen killed or missing. Not one hospital in the city was left in condition to shelter patients from the rain. The commanding general in the area and all his staff were killed, including 5,000 soldiers of a garrison of 8,000. The power and telephone service were cut off over the entire central region of the city. The streets were filled with debris, and thousands of fires burned unchecked among the injured and the dead.

In Hiroshima, according to a report by Dr. Robert Serber,

one walks for miles through a completely abandoned, forgotten and deserted desert of broken tile and rusty sheet iron—once the residential area. In the center of the city, all that remains are the shells of concrete buildings, with completely gutted interiors.

Nagasaki was an industrial city, with huge factories similar in construction to our own. From a distance, the parts of these factories still standing have a peculiarly drunken aspect—steel frames of buildings leaning far from the vertical, bent away from the point at which the bomb struck. Standing inside the remains, you are in the midst of a mass of twisted steel wreckage, tied in knots.

Japanese residential houses in both cities were almost completely wiped out to a distance of two miles from where the bomb struck. Minor damage extended to five miles. The destruction of life was so great that it will never be possible to know accurately how many people were killed.

Dr. Serber saw many corpses, many charred bodies, many piles of bones, and many patients with horrible burns. But he saw even more striking sights on the streets. He saw many people "who looked as if they had had a bad sunburn." On looking closely, however, one saw that "the burn might be only on one side of the face, or there might be a sharp shadow of a nose across the cheek, or the shadow of an ear." These were "shadows in reverse and gave a striking picture of how people were frozen in a set position when the bomb exploded. These shadows photographed the individual's actual position in relationship to the bomb."

In Nagasaki the factory buildings are situated in a valley surrounded on three sides by hills. Autumn came prematurely to the hills of this valley. The trees were yellow and brown with brilliant fall colors. The leaves were burned from the intense heat of the bomb. On the far side of the ridges of the valley, the trees retained their summer green, showing in sharp contrast the color these hills had been before.

Chief of Police Hirokuni Dazai, one of the Hiroshima survivors, saw "first a little spark, then a great flash. Trees swayed as in a great wind. Then my house fell down and started burning. The city was afire and the mountains were in flames. I tried to get into Hiroshima, a mile away, but I couldn't, because of the heat. Everything was scorched to the ground. Every living thing was blackened and dead—or waiting to die."

A Japanese newspaperman who arrived long before any American correspondents said he alighted from the train to find that the railway station, one of western Japan's largest, no longer existed. "There was a sweeping view right to the mountains north, south, and east—the city had vanished."

And to a small boy who saw it all, it was "very, very bright, like great big sun."

CHAPTER NINETEEN

FROM time immemorial man's strivings had been motivated by two dominant dreams. One was of a formula, called the philosophers' stone, for transmuting base metals into gold. The other was of an "elixir of life" that would keep him eternally young. Since gold symbolized wealth and power, which he considered essential for happiness, the quest for the philosophers' stone was not actually for gold *per se*, but for what the possession of great riches would bring him. It came in response to a deep-seated yearning in his psyche for dominance over man and power over the forces of nature, the longing to live up to his concept of himself as the dominant creature on earth.

These yearnings, which have manifested themselves under various disguises throughout the ages, are basically expressions of man's rebellion against the limitations of space and time. 'Way back in prehistoric times he invented the wheel as a device to narrow down his spatial limitations. His later inventions of the automobile and the airplane, the telegraph, the telephone, and radio, were manifestations of the same urge to conquer space. But conquest of space was not limited merely to getting places in a hurry. Basically it meant power over the material world existing in space, a power that only gold could give. Even greater than man's need to master space was his fundamental yearning to conquer time. Old age and death were always mocking at him. His gods were beings who neither were limited in space nor ever grew old. Thus man's eternal quest for the philosophers' stone and the elixir of life was actually a manifestation of his quest for means to conquer space and time. The philosophers' stone would make him lord of the material world in space; the elixir of life was to give him mastery over time and death.

After five hundred thousand to a million years of his existence on this earth, during which his quest had appeared under many metamorphoses, man at last is within striking distance of his goal. For atomic energy brings within sight the realization of the dream of the ages. He now has within his grasp a philosophers' stone that not only will transmute the elements and create wealth far greater in value than gold, but will also provide him with the means for gaining a far deeper insight into the mysteries of living processes, leading to the postponement of old age and the prolongation of life. This, in substance, is the true meaning of atomic energy harnessed in the service of mankind, as contrasted with its use in atomic bombs. It gives man the greatest chance he has ever had to master his material environment, to conquer space and time, disease and old age. He stands on Pisgah in the desert, gazing at a land of promise.

Before presenting a detailed explanation of these seemingly broad general statements it is necessary to clear up several popular misconceptions. The public has been fed fantastic fairy tales about small atomic-energy capsules "the size of a pea" that will drive automobiles and airplanes indefinitely, heat and light our homes and office buildings, run our refrigerators, radios, and air-conditioning systems, and furnish the power needed on the farm.

254

Atomic energy would run our factories, railroads, and steamships. Coal and petroleum would be used only for the chemicals that can be extracted from them for making perfumes, nylon stockings, aspirin, and similar substances. As our principal fuels for supplying heat, light, and power, coal and oil would be as out of date as the oxcart.

Now, all responsible scientists familiar with the matter agree that such claims are based on a lack of even an elementary acquaintance with the fundamental facts. Let us take the idea of the "power-pill" first. This is fundamentally impossible because to produce atomic energy, a basic minimum of uranium or plutonium (the only two substances that can be used at present for atomic energy) is absolutely essential. This basic amount is known, as already stated, as the "critical size." Anything less than this critical size will not yield any atomic energy, since if the amount is too small, the neutrons necessary to maintain the chain reaction would escape through the surface and be wasted.

How much is the critical amount? For the atomic bomb the amount, as we have seen, ranges from one to a hundred kilograms. In other words, anything less than one kilogram (2.2 pounds) of uranium 235 or plutonium would not work, and the critical amount may be as high as a hundred kilograms. Even one kilogram is not exactly a capsule.

But these critical amounts are for the production of an uncontrolled chain reaction with fast neutrons to release the energy at as high an explosive rate as possible. To use it for power we need a controlled reaction, which can be achieved only with slow neutrons. To slow down the neutrons, a moderator is necessary, which would weigh many times the amount of the U.235 or plutonium.

Nor is that all. The process of the release of atomic

energy is accompanied by the liberation of vast amounts of radioactivity, equivalent to that of many tons of radium. These radiations would instantly kill anyone coming near them. To protect one against their lethal effect, heavy shielding of two or three feet of steel or several times that amount of concrete is necessary. Together with the moderator, the shielding would make the weight of the unit wholly out of the question for automobiles or airplanes. Dr. Compton calculated that an atomic-energy plant delivering one hundred horsepower would weigh a minimum of fifty tons. Thus driving automobiles or airplanes by atomic power must be counted out as definitely impossible.

Even if these obstacles did not exist, it would still be highly undesirable from a political and social standpoint to permit possession of materials for atomic energy by individuals. Without question the greatest problem of our day is the proper control of atomic energy to prevent its use for destructive purposes. A small clique of intriguers at the head of a minor power, if they managed to get hold of sizable quantities of U.235 or plutonium, could do incalculable damage. With these substances placed indiscriminately in the hands of motorcar-owners, an international black market of enormous dimensions would be created and would make control out of the question.

The same reasons also apply to small power units on farms, and to the use of atomic power in locomotives. How about large steamships? It has been estimated that the cost of fuel is only twelve per cent of the cost of operating a 17,000-ton liner. Hence, even if it were possible from a technical and an engineering point of view to install atomic-energy power plants in steamships, as is not yet the case, it would still be impractical from an economic point of view. For battleships and submarines it might be worth while because it would eliminate the need of returning to base for refueling, but crews and even admirals will still have to eat, so they would have to come back to base sooner or later for food supplies.

Here another misconception must be cleared up. The impression has been created among the lay public that since we know how to use atomic energy in a bomb, we also could use it for peacetime power. This is far from being the case. The present atomic piles for the production of plutonium generate, it is true, tremendous amounts of heat. But this heat is of a low temperature, which cannot be used as a source of power. As Professor Smyth states: "An effective heat engine must not only develop heat but must develop heat at a high temperature. To run a chain-reacting system (i.e., atomic 'boiler') at a high temperature and to convert the heat generated to useful work is very much more difficult than to run a chain-reacting system at a low temperature."

At present we do not know how to run a chain-reacting system, the only system by which atomic energy can be released, at a high temperature. According to General Groves, who should know, it would take decades to develop such a system. Others, less pessimistic, believe it may be done in from three to ten years. But in the long run this will depend on how much effort, in money and resources, we are willing to devote to it. With the knowledge we have already gained it should not take more time to develop means for using atomic power for peacetime purposes than it did to harness it for military uses, provided the necesssity exists for the expenditure of large sums of money and for a large-scale national effort, as was the case with the atomic bomb.

This brings us up squarely against the economics of the question. In other words, to make such a concentrated national effort worth while we should have to know in advance that its successful outcome would lead to great savings in the present cost of light and power. The figures show that this would not be the case.

Dr. Leonard I. Katzin, of the atomic bomb group at the University of Chicago, states the problem this way: "By making the possibly incorrect assumption that the U.235 is consumed with the same efficiency as are the combustion fuels with which it is being compared (coal, oil, natural gas, etc.), and assuming that its efficiency of conversion into electrical energy is the same, we may obtain the following rough comparisons: In order to compete with bituminous coal at $5 a ton (approximately the 1942 wholesale average), a pound of U.235 must cost not more than $7,500. To compare with fuel oil at three cents a gallon, it must again be as low as $7,500. Competition with fifteen cent gasoline is effective at $37,500 a pound. To compete with artifical gas costing fifty cents a thousand cubic feet it may cost $40,000 a pound, while natural gas at the same price would demand a competition price of about $20,000 a pound."

These figures are based on the fact that one pound of U.235 releases the energy equivalent to 1,500 tons of coal, 250,000 gallons of fuel oil or gasoline, 80,000,000 cubic feet of artificial gas, or 40,000,000 cubic feet of natural gas.

The actual cost of a pound of concentrated U.235 cannot be revealed. Professor Dunning estimated that it would probably cost from $10,000 to $50,000 a pound to produce, depending on the process. But even assuming that we were to get the uranium free, the economies that would result would still be no more than between 3 and 17 per cent.

The reason is that fuel constitutes only a small percentage of the total power bill to the consumer. For example, the city dweller pays 3.5 cents per kilowatt-hour for his electricity. If the utility company were to pay nothing for the coal, it could afford to reduce his bill to 3.4 per kilowatt-hour. The cost of the coal is only three per cent of the total bill. The remainder pays for the costs of plant construction and maintenance, distribution, interest and profit charges, which would remain the same regardless of whether uranium or coal is used as the fuel. Even for large industrial power-users, the fuel cost is about 17 per cent of the total cost for power.

Dr. Katzin gives us further interesting comparisons between the total fuel consumption in the United States and the quantities of uranium available in the prewar years: In 1942, according to the Bureau of Mines, 649,000,000 tons of coal were mined and consumed, or the equivalent of about 216 tons of U.235. The production of natural gas for 1942 was three million million cubic feet, or the equivalent in energy of about 40 tons of U.235. Similar figures were calculated by Dr. Katzin for petroleum products. The capacity of the hydroelectric generating plants of the United States in 1942 was about 14,000,000 kilowatts, corresponding to a consumption of 1.23 pounds of U.235 every hour, or some five tons per year. Thus the total energy consumed in the United States per year is the equivalent of about 300 tons of U.235.

The large prewar producers of uranium were the United States, Canada, the Belgian Congo, and Czechoslovakia. Estimates published before the war indicated that a total of 20,000 tons of uranium was readily available. About half of this is located in the United States and Canada. Since each ton of uranium contains only 14 pounds of U.235, the figures show that there were only 140 tons of U.235 readily available in the world before the war. Even if all the uranium 238 were to be converted into plutonium for power purposes only, the supply would last only sixty-six years. Thorium, which is more abundant, cannot be used because it reacts only with fast neutrons, which makes it unavailable for power purposes. It could, however, be used in combination with uranium.

Of course, it is very likely that since the advent of the atomic bomb the world's uranium resources have greatly increased, but so has the demand for military purposes. In fact, in the present state of world affairs atomic power for peacetime purposes will for some time to come be closely linked with further developments on the international front. Every nation, large and small, will from now on try to get as much of it as it can lay its hands on. No metal in the world's history will be so jealously guarded or sought after. Overnight this substance, which had a pre-war market price of seven dollars per pound (this was for each pound of the element in the form of a nitrate, as there was no pure metal available) has become the most highly prized of all the natural elements, more precious than gold or any precious stone, more valuable than platinum or even radium.

Our coal resources, on the other hand, are estimated to last us for three to four thousand years. As for oil, though the supply may not last for more than fifty to a hundred years, there are methods now available for converting coal and natural gas into gasoline at a price no higher than current prices of the natural product.

Thus there are three fundamental reasons why we cannot expect large-scale use of atomic power in the immediate future:

1. It will require from five years to decades to develop the technology for constructing and operating high-temperature

atomic power piles. Plants totally different from those built for producing plutonium for atomic bombs must be designed, requiring the solution of problems much more difficult than those involved in building our atomic piles for low-temperature operation.

2. There is no economic incentive for investing the large sums required for developing such plants. For even if the uranium were free, which it certainly will not be, it would not lead to appreciable economies in the nation's power bill, since the cost of fuel represents only from 3 to 17 per cent of the total.

3. Lastly, the world's uranium supplies are strictly limited. Even if the United States were to have access to all the world's uranium, which, of course, is unthinkable, the supply would last only sixty-six years.

There is also the problem of the health hazard that will not incline communities to welcome atomic power plants in their vicinity. While the danger of an explosion in an atomic "boiler" would be about the same as in a steam plant, and could be made negligible if the plants are designed and handled by competent engineers, still there would always be the likelihood of an accident. Such an accident would be a catastrophe of the first magnitude, as the highly lethal radioactive materials that would be scattered over a large area by such an explosion would make it uninhabitable for some time.

Coal, oil, and rivers will therefore remain our principal sources of power for many years to come.

That does not mean, however, that atomic energy will not find any uses as a power source. On the contrary, it will undoubtedly have many highly important applications that no one at present could even guess at. But such uses will supplement, not supplant, our present abundant power sources. To use up our precious uranium for purposes that could be served equally well by our great coal and oil deposits and our great rivers would

261

be like washing dishes in the kitchen sink with a rare vintage of some precious wine.

One of the factors favoring an atomic pile as a power source is the promise it holds for greatly increased efficiency in the conversion of heat into work. As Dr. Katzin points out:

With ordinary fuels, the heat of reaction and rate of combustion set limits to the temperature which may be reached. In the case of the pile, the problem is to keep the temperature down to the limits set by the physical structure. Because of this characteristic, it is theoretically possible to operate a power cycle at such an elevated temperature that the efficiency of conversion of heat into work is greatly increased. The power output of atomic power installations per unit size [he adds] can be disproportionately high when compared with other types of sources. This coupling of small size and independence of large fuel supplies or watercourses gives the atomic pile certain unique values in situations in which these characteristics are important.

This view was further elucidated by Dr. Thomas. "The availability of power and the place where it is to be used is an important factor in considering any economic studies or prognostications of the power uses of the future.

For example [he said] in many manufacturing enterprises it is often the case that you have raw material available but no power, and that is a factor that must be counted on the optimistic side in bringing about atomic power plants in the future. This is particularly true in the mining industry where you have certain ores in isolated areas and no power for processing the ores. You could build an atomic power plant right on the site without the necessity of transmission lines. Such a situation allows you to pay more for power than in locations where you have abundant coal and oil on the spot.

Professor Morrison puts it this way:

Only if for special reasons the transportation of coal is impossible or prohibitively expensive will the substitution of atomic energy sources for ordinary fuels be made economically and on a reasonably large scale. Perhaps a hotel on the South Polar ice cap or in Arctic Siberia could afford an atomic power plant. The wind is after all a 'free' source of energy. But its reliable and large scale utilization is so expensive that we burn our heritage of coal rather than set up windmill plants on a great scale in the desert.

Thinking of atomic energy as just a concentrated fuel to serve as a substitute for coal or oil is to lose sight of its far more important implications as placing in the hands of man the greatest tool he has ever had given to him for making his world a much better place to live in, and to have a greater voice than he ever had before in the shaping of his destiny.

When the U.235 atoms are split in the atomic pile by the trillions, the resulting fragments are radioactive varieties of lighter elements. These elements do not exist in nature in radioactive form. They promise to become immensely valuable substances as substitutes for radium and X-rays and as catalysts in industrial processes. They are not promises for tomorrow. They are actualities, by-products of the creation of plutonium. They could be purified in large amounts if we want to build the plants for such purposes.

But the factor of the utmost significance, which dwarfs all other possible benefits that may result from man's new ability to liberate vast amounts of atomic energy, is the all-important fact that in the atomic pile man has at last a practically limitless source of neutrons. With these neutrons he can eventually transform his world and gain a mastery over space and time to a degree far greater than any of the ancient alchemists ever dreamed of achieving with their philosophers' stone and their elixir of life. For with the endless supply of neutrons at his disposal man can transmute practically

263

all the elements found in nature. He can create elements to order, elements that he could use for a better, richer, and more abundant life. Such elements could not be created in quantity by any other power on earth.

A number of these elements promise, among other things, to provide far more effective means for the treatment of cancer, and, better still, means that could serve to elucidate for the first time the mystery of the cause of the cancer. Once the cause is determined, means for its prevention, or even its cure, are likely to be found.

For example, it is known that certain elements have affinities for particular organs of the body and could therefore be used for treating diseases of those organs. Iodine, for instance, has an affinity for the thyroid gland; phosphorus for the bone marrow, where the blood cells are formed; strontium for the bone structure. It had therefore been known a long time that if such substances could be made radioactive they could be fed to the body in small amounts in the treatment of cancer of the thyroid, leukemia (a form of cancer of the white blood cells), and cancer of the bone, respectively. Small amounts of these substances were made artifically radioactive by the cyclotron and used with good effect on cancer patients.

Similarly, ordinary table salt was transmuted by the cyclotron in small amounts and used in the treatment of other forms of internal cancer. Such substances have the same effect as radium and are even more powerful than the natural substance, with the advantage that they can be selected because of their special affinity for particular organs and administered internally, either by injection or by mouth. This, of course, is impossible with radium. Unfortunately, the cyclotron, a big and expensive machine, could produce only minute amounts of these substances, far short of the need. In the atomic pile, however, we have a neutron factory equivalent to more than a million of the most powerful cyclotrons. We can now produce these life-saving substances in practically limitless amounts at an extremely low cost, within the reach of the poorest of cancer patients.

Important as this is, there are still more important things to come from the philosophers' stone, or elixir of life, if you will, within the neutron. For with these neutrons man can create practically limitless quantities of radioactive forms of the four basic elements of life— hydrogen, carbon, nitrogen, and oxygen. By incorporating minute amounts of these easily distinguishable atoms into the food molecules of animals and plants, it becomes possible, for the first time on a large scale, to trace their course step by step in the body of the living animal and growing plant. These "tagged atoms" will serve as a "lantern" in the dark labyrinth of life. Processes hitherto hidden, normal as well as abnormal, will stand revealed at long last.

This is of the utmost significance for man's future welfare and cannot be overestimated or overemphasized. If the atomic bomb does not bring doomsday first, this lantern into life will set man on the road to the millennium.

Men and plants live by the food they eat. When the food enters the living body of plant or animal, it is broken up into constituent parts and utilized for energy and for the replacement of burned-up tissue. This process is known as metabolism. It is as complex as life itself and is, in fact, a synonym for life, for life is metabolism. The processes of metabolism are different in normal health from those in disease, and each disease is characterized by specific abnormalities in metabolism. If we could only know what these abnormalities are, we should have a better insight into the nature of the disease and a much better approach to its prevention and treatment.

The tagged atoms of the basic elements of life that we can now create by atomic energy will enable us to trace what the animal and plant body does with its food at every stage of digestion and incorporation into the living body. They can be used in harmless amounts in all living things, including man. By studying first normal metabolism and then comparing it with that in the various diseases, biology, medicine, physiology and biochemistry, working together, would learn for the first time what deviations occur in the sick body and take intelligent measures to prevent and correct these deviations.

Take cancer, for example. We have but a very sketchy idea of the metabolism of the cancer cell and how it deviates from the normal cell. By tracing the food taken in by the cancer patient we can now find out what stuff the cancer cell uses for its building blocks. We could trace every step in which these building blocks are made, the elements of which they are composed, the sources whence they come. Suppose it is found that these sources are present only in certain foods. Then the feeding of a diet in which these elements are missing would starve the cancer to death.

This could be done not only with cancer but with all other diseases. For the first time we may be able to establish the metabolism in every type of disease, both chronic and acute. We may elucidate at last the mystery of arteriosclerosis, arthritis, heart disease, diseases of the kidney, and most other baffling ills that are taking a tremendous toll in death and suffering.

At last we stand on the threshold of elucidating the mystery of why we get old. As we age, our metabolism gradually changes, but how we do not know. By feeding animals throughout their lifespan foods in which these tagged atoms have been incorporated, as well as feeding them to human beings who have reached a ripe old age without impairment of faculties, we might find out what it is that makes people old, and the way will have been opened for an intelligent approach to means for postponing the process.

And that is only part of the picture. With new types of tagged atoms we at last have a means that promises to solve one of the major mysteries of nature, the process whereby plants, by the use of the green coloring substance named chlorophyll (the stuff that makes the grass green), are able to harness the energy of the sun. Chlorophyll is the only substance known in nature that somehow possesses the power to act as a sunlight trap. It catches the energy of sunlight and stores it up in the plant. Without this ability no life could exist on earth. We obtain the energy we need for living from the solar energy stored up in the plant food we eat, or in the flesh of the animals that eat the plants. The energy we obtain from coal or oil is solar energy trapped by the chlorophyll in plant life millions of years ago. We live by the sun through the agency of chlorophyll. By means of the sunlight trapped by the chlorophyll the plant is able to synthesize starches, sugars, and proteins out of the carbon dioxide and water in the air and the minerals in the soil. Thus our supply of energy for living and power for running our civilization are both made possible by this mysterious substance that makes grass green.

So far the process whereby chlorophyll traps the energy of the sun has eluded the searches of the world's greatest scientists. Dr. Conant, before he became president of Harvard, was among those who tried to solve the mystery. The process is just as complicated as life itself.

Now, carbon dioxide is one of the basic elements used by chlorophyll in building its trap for the sun. With the powerful stream of neutrons now at our command in the atomic boiler we can create large quantities of a new type of carbon, of atomic weight 14, which does not exist in nature. We can incorporate this new carbon in carbon dioxide and feed it to the plant. We can then watch it at each step of the process as it builds up its sunlight trap.

With this, two tremendous vistas of incalculable importance will open up. By learning how the plant builds up its food substance from carbon dioxide, water, and a few minerals (we could also build these other substances out of tagged elements) we may learn to use the same substances and sunlight for the direct production of food. We would no longer be dependent exclusively on the soil to give us our daily bread. Man at last may be able to produce enough food to provide abundantly for the world's population. The nitrogen in the atmosphere, the water in his rivers, some of the common elements in the soil and in the sea, will be the raw materials out of which he will grow his foods.

The other vista is equally alluring. Learning how the plant traps the sunlight may lead to the building of a better trap. The way may be opened to harnessing the enormous energy poured down on the earth every second by the sun, only a small fraction of which is now utilized by us indirectly through the chlorophyll in plants. Thus atomic energy, while not providing us directly with a great new reservoir of power, promises to bring the sun down to earth as its gift to man.

It also promises, in more than a figurative sense, to bring the moon and Mars, and other neighbors in space, within man's reach, for here at last he has a fuel powerful enough to free him from the gravitational bonds of the earth. All existing fuels have only a little more than the energy needed to lift their own weight beyond the earth's gravitational field. Hence no rocket or space-ship that would leave the earth could hitherto be made, as no existing fuel has enough power to lift both its own weight and the weight of the rocket to a point beyond the reach of the earth's attractive force.

In the atomic bomb, on the other hand, there is more than a million times the energy needed to get beyond the earth's field of gravity. This, therefore, opens the possibility of sending a rocket or space-ship to the moon, or even Mars. Man for the first time has the fuel for such a space-ship. He still lacks the engine to utilize this cosmic fire. While scientists point to formidable obstacles still to be overcome in the solution of the propulsion problem, they do not regard them as basically insurmountable.

The interplanetary era may not yet be just around the corner, but it is already faintly discernible above the horizon. And the real shape of things yet to come may still be hidden beyond the horizon.

In the words of Dr. Compton:

Fifty years ago it could not be predicted that X-rays would become a powerful weapon in the fight against cancer, or that researches made possible by X-rays would reveal the electron, and with it give us the radio and a host of electronic devices. Such unforeseen developments are the result of every great discovery. It would be surprising similarly if the really important consequences of the release of atomic energy are not in directions as yet unpredicted.

We stand at the gateway to a new world.

CHAPTER TWENTY

ON that historic morning in the desert of New Mexico when the first atomic bomb sent up a mountain of cosmic fire 41,000 feet into the stratosphere and suffused the earth with a light never before seen under the sun, your world and mine, the world we knew, came to an end. A new world was born in that mountain of fire. What kind of world this new world is going to be no one yet knows. But we do know that it could be a vastly better world than the one that has just come to an end. Whether the vast potentialities of this new world will ever be turned into actuality, in whole or even in part, will largely depend on what the inhabitants of this new world, you and I, make of it. That is the most important matter for all of us to think about, today, tomorrow, and in the years to come. Mankind now has the greatest chance it ever had in the million years of its existence on this earth. If it muffs this chance it may never get another.

The tragic truth is that at present we really cannot be sure that the war is over. Twenty-five years from now, or even sooner, we may find out that what we thought was the end of the war was no more than merely another prolonged armistice, a period in which we took time out to stock up with bigger and better atomic bombs. If that happens the end cannot be far away.

To Dr. Kistiakowski the bursting of the first atomic bomb was "the nearest thing to Doomsday." To me, who saw the same thing, the spectacle meant the birth of a new world. Which one of us was right? That again is for the inhabitants of this new world to decide.

These two attitudes were poignantly illustrated to me in a striking symbolic form in the explosions at New Mexico and Nagasaki. In the first the mountain that rose above the clouds took the form for a fleeting instant of a gigantic Statue of Liberty, its arm raised to the sky, symbolizing the birth of a new freedom for man. At Nagasaki the multicolored cloud assumed at one stage of its evolution the form of a giant totem pole, a "living totem pole carved with many grotesque masks grimacing at the earth" and at its inhabitants, symbolizing an atavistic throw-back to primitive savagery and barbarism.

Future generations, if there are to be future generations, may look upon the harnessing of atomic energy as the greatest single milestone in man's material progress, in the course of his everlasting battle to harness nature's forces to make possible a decent life for himself on this earth. But while this development may mean man's greatest scientific triumph, it may also mean the most tragic moment in his history—a moment in which we may be standing on the brink of the great abyss. For all man's recent ills have been brought about by the misuse of the products of man's genius. If mankind sees to it that atomic energy is properly controlled, this new cosmic fire can bring him new light and new warmth and new freedom. If he allows it to get out of control, as was the case with man's other inventions, it will mean a conflagration that will engulf the earth and all its inhabitants, leaving abysmal chaos and ruin.

271

Mankind must now face the reality that atomic energy is here to stay. The question is: Are we? If we are, we must find means to control it. On that will depend whether atomic energy is to mean a horn of super-plenty or a super-box of Pandora. Man, like Hamlet, must ask himself the question: To be or not to be? There can be only one defense against the atomic bomb—peace. On that all our scientists agree. The word "peace" has become synonymous with survival. The word "war" has become synonymous with suicide.

Peace or atomic war? That is the question the world is facing. But only the peoples of the world can supply the answer. It will not, it cannot, be answered by us alone. No unilateral decision can supply the answer.

While no military defense against the atomic bomb is envisaged by our scientists, there is one instrumentality, actually two instrumentalities in one, that can conquer the atomic bomb and put it to use as man's slave, not his master. These instrumentalities are the human brain and the human heart, man's mind and man's spirit. It was the combination of the human mind and the human spirit that created the atomic bomb against insuperable obstacles. The creators of the atomic bomb are greater than the thing they created.

We must therefore start with faith in the mind and in the spirit of man. Without this faith no methods of control, no organization, will succeed, for no human institutions can thrive on a foundation of suspicion and distrust. James Russell Lowell said: "Be noble and the nobility dormant in your neighbor will rise to meet yours." Suspicion breeds suspicion. Nobility engenders nobility.

We must start with faith in the ultimate triumph of the good and in the fulfillment of man's destiny on earth as an innately noble creature.

272

OF THE ATOMIC BOMB

Prometheus was the first scientist. He invented fire, the symbol of light, and gave it to man, thereby starting him on his march to civilization. Zeus, the Olympian, symbolized the tyrant who made man his slave. He knew that fire would make man free. So he chained Prometheus, the liberator of man, to the rock, and set the vulture, symbolizing war and strife between men, to torture him.

All through the history of civilization this ancient struggle between Prometheus, the liberator, and Zeus, the enslaver, has been going on. There have been periods of enlightenment, such as the Golden Age of ancient Greece, the Renaissance, and the nineteenth century, in which Prometheus succeeded in breaking his chains. These may be called the Prometheus Unbound periods.

The world is now witnessing a new period, in which Zeus, the tyrant and enslaver, is threatening to chain Prometheus, the liberator, once more to the rock and to put all mankind back into bondage.

The word Prometheus, translated from the Greek, means "forethought," thinking ahead. If we bring our concentrated thought to bear upon this problem, Prometheus will remain free. With this forethought, if we keep thinking ahead, and think clearly and objectively, in a spirit of faith in the destiny of man, this great new force placed at our disposal can become the greatest weapon for enforcing peace the world has ever known, ensuring a period of peace lasting conceivably until a time when the groundwork has been laid for a world government.

In the final analysis it is the American people who have opened up this great new continent of atomic power. Destiny has placed its trust in our people by providing us with the key to this hitherto tightly locked "cosmic cupboard," and the American people must, and

273

will, keep faith with this trust. We must develop and cultivate this continent into a new promised land of plenty, for ourselves and for all mankind, bringing in a new era of wealth, health, and happiness such as the world has never seen.

But the time at present is still 9.15; it is still 12.01. It is no longer Japanese time, it is world time. It is 9.15 over the civilized world. It is 12.01 on the hour-glass of history.

CHAPTER TWENTY-ONE

AT nine o'clock on Monday morning, July 1, 1946 (Bikini time), the atomic bomb made its first appearance on the world stage on Bikini Lagoon, Marshall Islands, 2,000 miles southwest of Hawaii, and 4,150 miles from San Francisco. It was the fourth to explode in less than a year, but whereas the first three had been dropped at strictly private performances shrouded in wartime secrecy, this time the eyes and ears of the world were watching and listening.

From the skydeck of the U.S.S. *Appalachian*, some twenty miles away, I watched the pillar of cosmic fire rise to a height of seven miles. To some of the newspapermen aboard, keyed up to the point of expecting the observation ship to be blown out of the water, the spectacle, obscured somewhat by an intervening white cloud, was a disappointment. To me, who could distinguish between the natural cloud and the atomic cloud, the sight was awesome and spine-chilling. Through the haze I could see a boiling, angry, super-volcano struggling toward the sky, belching forth enormous masses of iridescent flames and smoke, and giant rings of rainbow, at times giving the appearance of a monster tugging at the earth in an effort to lift it and hurl it to another point in space. It was like

275

watching the birth and death of a star, born and disintegrated in the instant of its birth.

About an hour before "bombs away," an electrically operated metronome, placed on the battleship *Pennsylvania* and hooked up to a radio transmitter, started ticking away the last minutes. Its beat, which sounded more and more like drums in the jungle, could be heard on the radio by the listening world. Coming from the deserted fleet of nearly a hundred ships in the Bikini Lagoon, its "crews" consisting of some three thousand goats, pigs, and mice, the time interval between beats seemed to grow longer as the zero hour drew near. To me, listening through my earphones, the metronome drowned out the throbbing of the ship's engines and the pulsings of the Pacific. It came to sound like a voice of doom tolling off the world's last minutes.

Then, amid the ticking, came a human voice that seemed to fill all space, a staccato voice that spoke with a tone of finality:

"Thirty minutes to go! Thirty minutes to go!" Then silence, through which the tone of the metronome could be heard again.

Twenty minutes passed and the voice spoke again:

"Ten minutes to go! Ten minutes to go!"

Thrice more the voice drowned out the metronome:

"Five minutes to go! Five minutes to go!"

"Two minutes to go! Two minutes to go!"

"One minute to go! One minute to go!"

Each time the voice repeated itself like an echo.

Then a voice said: "Bomb away!" and on the radio at the same time came another voice:

"Listen, world, this is Crossroads!"

Through my dark goggles, which I took off immediately after the flash, I saw a reddish-purple ball of fire, smaller than the one I had seen in New Mexico, shooting

276

upward like a meteor going in the wrong direction. It was quickly surrounded by a gigantic spherical envelope of fog. The envelope collapsed with great violence, like a balloon punctured by an invisible hand. Out of it, like a monster hatched from a giant egg, emerged a mushroom-topped cloud. At the cloud's base the collapsed sphere of condensed fog became a gigantic ring of white smoke that kept expanding outward. The mushroom-topped cloud grew, kept playing hide-and-seek with the natural white cloud, ever changing color and form, until it reached 35,000 feet. The top then broke away from the main stem and floated off.

This was the first act of "Operations Crossroads," a drama originally scheduled by its impresario, joint Army-Navy-Air-Force Task Force One, under command of Vice Admiral W. H. P. Blandy, to be played in three acts—Test Able, Test Baker, and Test Charlie. Test Able was to determine the effect of an atomic bomb dropped from an airplane and exploded over a specially arranged target fleet at a height of several hundred feet. Test Baker was to find what an atomic bomb exploded under water at a relatively shallow depth would do to a fleet anchored in a harbor. Test Charlie was to be a deep-water test, to probe its effect on a fleet in the open sea. The curtain rose on Test Baker at 8.35 on the morning of July 25, 1946, Marshall Islands time. When the curtain fell and the score was tallied, Test Charlie, scheduled for March 1947, was called off on orders of President Truman. Able and Baker had told the story. Very little more, if anything, could be learned from Charlie.

The last stages of preparation for Test Baker began on the day prior to the actual performance, when the weatherman informed Admiral Blandy that the winds and clouds would be propitious. As was the case at a similar time before Able day, the weatherman's green light set in motion men and ships and planes over a vast area of thousands of square miles, an operation of a magnitude and complexity equivalent to a major battle. More than 40,000 men and 169 ships of all types, not counting the guinea-pig fleet of 87 ships, began moving out of the Bikini Lagoon to their various preassigned stations. Thousands of these men, members of the skeleton crews aboard the target vessels, had to be transferred to other ships, and more than 10,000 instruments, from the simplest to the most complex, were given a last-minute check-up.

All through the day and late into the night and the early hours of the morning the non-target ships kept moving out of the lagoon into the open sea. All along the horizon one could see an endless line of lights moving silently through the darkness, a city of light fleeing the fury of atomic fire that was to start on the morrow. Watching them, one was thankful that this was a peace-time maneuver, but one could not help thinking that this might be a rehearsal for doomsday. One visualized the endless line of fugitives less than a year before from Hiroshima and Nagasaki, the dead on the march.

As what had been designated as "Mike-hour" approached, the air became alive with planes—giant B-29's, and C-54's, Navy Hellcats and torpedo planes, Flying Fortresses and huge flying boats—all flying in perfect group formations over definite areas in concentric circles at varying predetermined altitudes; each assigned to some specific task, to be carried out at the proper time in a matter of seconds. There were the Army and Navy "drones," pilotless planes guided by mother ships in the air, designated to fly through the atomic whirlwind at various points, high and low. Some of the drones, escorted by control planes, came from Shangri-La, the carrier, some forty miles away. With the possible exception of

Able day, Test Baker displayed the greatest aggregation of automatic devices in history. It was "Robot's day" at Bikini, foreshadowing a much greater "Robot's day" over the world.

Able and Baker were the most photographed events in history, with a total of about five hundred cameras of all types used to photograph an event that took place in terms of millionths of a second. The cameras at Bikini took more than 50,000 stills and 1,500,000 feet of motion-picture film. One, the world's largest aerial camera, used a 48-inch focal-length telephoto lens capable of taking a legible photograph of the dial of a wrist watch a quarter of a mile away. One high-speed motion-picture camera operated at the rate of 1,000 pictures per second. These high-speed cameras had to be operated electronically by remote control and, since the amount of film they could carry was good for but a few seconds, required a very intricate special system to be set in operation at the proper split second.

In the hours before dawn the lagoon was a dark void surrounded by a large circle of light. Only a few men remained, to add the final touches to "Mr. Baker's make-up." This done, they began the ritual of setting the stage for his appearance. The stage was a specially equipped barge. In its center was an "altar" provided with a trap-door. Garbed in watertight raiment, "Great God Baker" was gingerly placed on the "altar" and lowered into the dark waters of the lagoon, to a depth estimated at fifty to ninety feet.

The last members of the human species then climbed aboard the mystery ship on which Mr. Baker had been made ready and silently rode away. The only forms of higher life left in the lagoon "to man the fleet" were twenty pigs and four hundred mice.

Two hours before "Mike-hour" a voice from the

279

Cumberland Sound, the control ship from which Mr. Baker was to be sparked by a trained electron, began booming out the time signals. The ship carried the code name "Abraham" and the voice thus kept identifying itself as the "voice of Abraham." It was the official time-keeper, co-ordinating all the various activities. It began counting off the hours, then the minutes, and then the seconds. Then the voice of Abraham yelled: "Fire!" and at the same instant a great gigantic white sun, about ten times larger than the natural sun, jumped out of the waters of the lagoon, and more than forty thousand men beheld a new revelation.

The super-sun quickly exploded into a mass of clouds, and out of the clouds came, first, a quivering mountain, lighted up from within by a dazzling white light. At the summit of this mountain there again appeared a gigantic, boiling, shimmering mushroom, which, though lower in height than the mushrooms of the earlier atomic clouds, was many times greater in diameter. It kept changing in shape, form, and color so rapidly that it was difficult for the human eye and the human mind to grasp it all. Indeed, even the official pictures of this most photographed event in history have managed to give but a faint approximation of the event's magnitude.

For a time it looked as though a continent had risen from the sea, as though we were watching the repetition of a phenomenon that took place when the earth was young. We saw the sea belch forth a chain of mountains glistening in the sun. Then the mountains were metamorphosed and fused into a giant tree, spreading out in all directions, bearing many invisible fruits deadly to man —alpha particles, electrons, positrons, neutrons, gamma rays—fruits of the tree of knowledge, which man may eat only at his peril.

I watched the spectacle from the deck of the "Big

280

Apple," as the U.S.S. *Appalachian* was known to its crew and passengers, at a distance of only eight miles. This time we were not required to wear dark goggles, which had spoiled the spectacle for so many on Able day. The day was clear, and with the aid of binoculars we could clearly see the great ships of the target fleet, the red-painted *Nevada*, the *Arkansas*, the *Pennsylvania*, the *New York*, the carrier *Saratoga*, the once mighty Japanese battleship *Nagato*, the hulk of the carrier *Independence*, shattered by the Able-day blast, the former German cruiser *Prinz Eugen*, cruisers, destroyers, transports, landing craft, and floating drydocks. We kept our binoculars focused on the *Arkansas*, for we had guessed that she had been chosen this time as the target ship. Good old *Arkansas*, I had visited her only three days before and drunk some excellent coffee in her wardroom, scene of many councils of war during the days of her grandeur when she carried the fighting traditions of our Navy on the seven seas, from Normandy to Iwo Jima and Okinawa. In her long log, dating back to 1910, is proudly mentioned the fact that she was present at the meeting of President Roosevelt and Prime Minister Churchill at Argentia, Newfoundland, when the Atlantic Charter was drafted.

When the cloud that had covered nearly the entire fleet had lifted, the first thing that we all noticed was that the *Arkansas* was no longer there. The *Nagato* and "Old Sara" were listing. Many of the ships appeared to have been displaced from their moorings and pushed about the lagoon like toy boats. Yet these were mere first impressions of the story as it unfolded itself over the days, weeks, and months that have passed since. Some of the story may not be known for years to come.

A leisurely examination of the pictures revealed a dome, lighted from within by incandescent materials, rising upon the surface of the lagoon. The blast, they showed, was followed by an opaque cloud, which rapidly enveloped about half of the target array. The cloud vanished in about two seconds, to reveal a column of ascending water. From some of the photographs it appears that this column "lifted the 26,000-ton battleship *Arkansas* for a brief interval before the vessel plunged to the bottom of the lagoon."

The diameter of the column of water, which formed the main stem of the mushroom, was about 2,200 feet, while the height of the stem was about 5,500. The spray which formed the mushroom's head rose to a height of about two miles, and its diameter, which grew at breathtaking speed, reached at least five miles. For several minutes after the column reached maximum height, water kept falling back, forming an expanding cloud of spray that swallowed up the ships. A wall of foaming water several hundred feet high surrounded the base of the column. Waves outside the water column, about 1,000 feet from the center of the explosion, were thirty to a hundred feet high. These waves rapidly diminished in size as they proceeded outward, the highest wave reaching Bikini Island, some three and a half miles away, measuring seven feet.

The weight of the column of water lifted into the air was conservatively estimated at 10,000,000 tons. The spray and the foaming circle of water at the base brought the total weight of the water lifted by the energy liberated by the underwater explosion to well over 15,000,000 tons. Since the entire United States wartime fleet was somewhere around 11,000,000 tons, the power of the bomb was thus great enough to lift that huge fleet, more than twice greater than the combined tonnage of all the world's prewar navies, to a height of about a mile out of the water. The *Arkansas,* though it was "well over" five hundred feet away from the explosion, was just like a

282

cork on top of an erupting volcano. And all this by the conversion of about one gram of matter into energy.

For more than two hours on Baker day we stood and watched "Old Sara" die, inch by inch, till she finally disappeared. Five days later we woke up to find that the *Nagato,* with its strange pagoda towering in the center, was no longer there. And fully five months later the *Prinz Eugen* gave up the ghost. Many more ships were damaged. But the full story of Mr. Baker's rampage is still unfolding itself as more facts come to light.

The Able-day bomb missed the target, the battleship *Nevada,* by a wide margin. The location of the burst, accurately determined from photographs, was such that only one ship was within a thousand feet of the surface point over which the bomb exploded. There were about twenty ships within half a mile, all of which were badly damaged, many being put out of action, and five sunk. It required up to twelve days to repair all of those ships left afloat sufficiently so that they could have steamed under their own power to a major port for repair.

Measurements of radiation intensity and a study of the animals exposed on the ships in Test Able, the Joint Chiefs of Staff Evaluation Board reported to the President, "show that the initial flash of principal lethal radiations, which are gamma rays and neutrons, would have killed almost all personnel normally stationed aboard the ships centered around the air burst and many others at greater distances."

Similarly, the Joint Chiefs reported, the Baker-day explosion produced intense radioactivity in the waters of the lagoon. The radioactivity immediately after the burst was estimated "to have been equivalent of many hundreds of tons of radium." A "few minutes exposure to this intense radiation at its peak would, within a brief interval, have incapacitated human beings and have resulted in their death within days or weeks." Great quantities of radioactive water descended upon the ships from the column or were thrown over them by waves. This highly lethal radioactive water constituted such a hazard that for more than a month after Baker day it was still unsafe for inspection parties to spend any useful length of time at the center of the target area or to board ships anchored there.

It was not until September that the score in terms of damage to ships could be tallied. It was found that all but nine of the ninety-two target ships and craft in the two tests were either sunk, damaged, or contaminated by radioactivity. The nine that escaped with negligible damage and in serviceable conditions consisted of four submarines and five transports. Not a single major ship escaped. And the reason that more of them were not sunk was, firstly, that the first bomb missed its target by a wide margin, and, secondly, that, as Admiral Blandy repeatedly pointed out, many of the ships were deliberately placed so they would not receive the full blast, in order to leave something for the scientists to study.

However, to evaluate properly the two tests in the Bikini Lagoon it is not enough to determine the effects of the atomic bomb on naval vessels of various types artificially placed at varying distances from the center of the explosion. Scientists and others closely connected with the development of the bomb, who know its potentialities for wholesale destruction and who are devoting their energies to arouse public awareness of the danger confronting civilization, stood aghast at the change of the public's attitude, following the Bikini tests, toward the greatest problem facing mankind.

Before Bikini the world stood in awe of this new cosmic force which, concentrated in one rather small package, could destroy a large city, kill and maim hundreds of thousands, and bring the surrender of an army of five million without firing a shot. After Bikini this feeling of awe had largely evaporated and had been supplanted by a sense of relief unrelated to the grim reality of the situation. Having lived with a nightmare for nearly a year, the average citizen was only too glad to believe in any pipe dream to regain his peace of mind.

He had been led to expect that one bomb would sink the entire Bikini fleet, kill all the animals aboard, make a hole in the bottom of the ocean, and create tidal waves that would be felt for thousands of miles. He had even been told that every one of the 42,000 participating in the test would die. Since none of these things happened, he was only too eager to conclude that the atomic bomb was, after all, just another weapon. As such, Mr. Average Citizen felt, it was a problem concerning only the military and nothing for him to be worried about.

That such an attitude was very far removed from the grim reality was revealed in the reports to President Truman by his two evaluation boards. Nevertheless, it is doubtful that these reports were sufficient to undo the damage. This factor in itself may far outweigh whatever gains may have been derived from the Bikini tests. For if there is anything the world needs, it is a reawakening of its consciousness to the fact that the atomic bomb is not just another weapon against which our military minds will find a defense, but the greatest cataclysmic force ever released on earth, and that unless some means are found for its effective control, it will inevitably lead to the destruction of civilization.

Despite the unanimous warnings of the leading scientists who developed the bomb and know its potentialities for even greater destructiveness, this appalling fact had not yet fully impressed itself on the hearts and minds of the peoples of the world when the Bikini tests were made.

285

Nor, judging by their remarks, had it been fully grasped by the representatives of some of the world's leading nations. At this point the Bikini tests diverted, at least temporarily, the world's attention from the greatest danger that ever faced it. Wasn't "Pig 311" found swimming in the lagoon several hours after being blown into the water? Doesn't that prove that the atomic bomb had been grossly overrated? The grim lessons of Hiroshima and Nagasaki were all but obliterated by the image of a swimming pig.

What the reports by the President's two evaluation boards did not emphasize is that future wars, if not prevented, will not employ atomic bombs singly, but by the hundreds and thousands. Dr. Oppenheimer has stated that in the not too distant future atomic bombs will be easy to make and will cost not more than one million dollars each. There is enough uranium and thorium in the earth's crust to manufacture them by the thousands, once adequate plants have been built. And while the so-called "know-how" of their manufacture is now possessed largely by us, it is generally agreed that it will take only a relatively short time—five to ten years—before other nations will have it.

The Bikini tests have yielded another lesson of the utmost significance to our strategists that is not touched on in the reports to the President. As I watched the clouds of death that spread over the Bikini fleet, it became obvious to me that amphibious invasions such as those of North Africa, Italy, and Normandy would be impossible against an enemy possessing atomic bombs. A few atomic bombs exploded in the air and under water would not only sink all the invasion craft but also kill every man aboard. Those who by miracle might escape the blast and the heat would surely die from the invisible, all-penetrating radiation. Moreover, had the Germans possessed an atomic bomb they would not have had to wait until the invasion got under way. They could have destroyed all of England before the invasion could have been organized.

Another vital fact must be impressed on the public mind and on the consciousness of some of the world's statesmen who still seem to think and talk and, what is still worse, act, in terms of pre-atomic diplomacy. The atomic bomb is not primarily a tactical weapon against armies, or against navies or task forces spread out over miles of ocean, but is the ideal terror weapon, to be used strategically for the wholesale destruction of cities, industries, and populations. In the case of an atomic war against the United States, an enemy could well afford to ignore the existence of our Navy at sea. As Dr. Oppenheimer has testified, a rain of atomic bombs could wipe out 40,000,000 of our population in one night.

Such an attack would destroy most of our vital industrial centers and the industries where the sinews of war are produced, including all the vital equipment for the Army and Air Forces, the shells for the Navy's guns, torpedoes, electrical machinery, and all the other paraphernalia without which a modern army, navy, or air force could not exist. It would also destroy the harbors to which all ships must eventually return for repairs and supplies, as well as the naval bases and supply depots. Deprived of these, ships at sea would be left completely helpless after their supplies of ammunition, food, and fuel had been exhausted.

Furthermore, while the Bikini tests have given us some lessons considered valuable, they have also furnished valuable lessons to a potential enemy. We have revealed to him, at great expense to ourselves, that one atomic bomb exploded in the air "does great harm to superstructures of major ships within a half-mile radius" and that "no ship

287

within a mile could have escaped without some damage to itself and serious injury to a large number of its crew." We have further revealed to him that "unprotected personnel within one mile of an air-burst atomic bomb would suffer high casualties by intense neutron and gamma radiation as well as by blast and heat," whereas the submarine explosion could sink a battleship well over 500 feet away, an aircraft carrier more than 1,000 feet away, and another battleship about 1,500 feet away. (The last two distances are conservative estimates based on personal observation. Foreign naval experts present no doubt made more accurate estimates.) We have, moreover, informed him that in addition to doing great damage to hulls, the underwater explosion threw about 10,000,000 tons of highly radioactive water on the decks and into the hulls of vessels so that "the contaminated ships became radioactive stoves" that "would have burned all living things aboard them with invisible and painless but deadly radiation."

With this information as a blueprint, an enemy would thus know how to use atomic bombs against a fleet in a harbor. He would know just how many bombs he would need and how to space them to destroy the harbor and the ships and all living things aboard them, and, for good measure, the people and the city in which the harbor is located.

It must also be remembered that it is not likely that atomic bombs in a war some fifteen or twenty years hence would be dropped from an airplane at high altitude or be surreptitiously planted in a city or under water. The development of the V-2 rocket makes it more probable that before long the long-range guided missile, hurtling at 5,000 miles per hour at altitudes of several hundred miles, will become the choice method for dealing swift death to cities and populations.

288

These are the sober facts that the peoples and statesmen of the world must keep constantly in mind. In the words of President Truman's Civilian Evaluation Board, "as was demonstrated by the terrible havoc wrought at Hiroshima and Nagasaki, the Bikini tests strongly indicate that future wars employing atomic bombs may well destroy nations and change present standards of civilization. To us who have witnessed the devastating effects of these tests, it is evident that if there is to be any security or safety in the world, war must be eliminated as a means of settling differences among nations."

The atom-bomb air-burst on Able day over the fleet at Bikini. Photo from a Navy patrol bomber flying just beyond range of explosion. Cloud is thirty-five miles high.

The Atomic Age begins:
5.30 a.m., July 16, 1945,
at Zero,
Alamogordo, New Mexico.

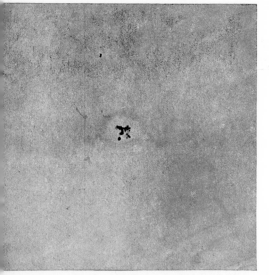

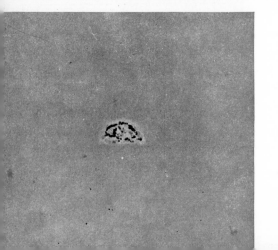

Dawn Over Zero:
Stages in test explosion,
New Mexico.

One cubic mile of atomic fog obscures Bikini target fleet on Baker day. Photo by automatic camera on a near-by island.

Cloud formation on Baker day at peak, shortly before the rapid disintegration of the mushroom as the column of water starts to fall.

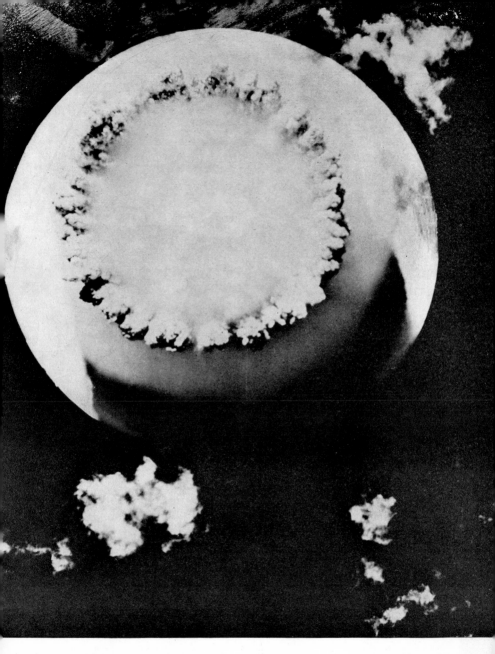

The Baker-day explosion. Water, steam, and radioactive substances released in the blast boil skyward. Photo from a plane almost directly overhead at the instant of detonation.

The Able-day explosion a few seconds after detonation. Underwater pressure-wave, seen as a black band, moves toward shore. Photo by automatic camera in tower on an atoll.

The end of the old aircraft carrier *Saratoga* a few hours after the Baker-day blast.

The atomic derby of water, spray, and steam, formed in the initial stages of the Baker-day explosion.

Ten million tons of water hurled 6,000 feet into the air by the atom bomb on Baker
day. The column is fully 2,200 feet in diameter, and is moving upward with such
incredible speed that its mottled appearance could be caught only on this remarkable short-exposure photograph. The condensation cloud on top of column now

covers an area of ten square miles. The dark hole on right of column is believed to
be the battleship *Arkansas*, lifted into the air before it sank within a matter of
seconds after the burst. Column enters first stage of characteristic mushroom.

Hiroshima at 9.15 : Air view before bombing.

Hiroshima at 9.15 : Air view after bombing.

Hiroshima. Looking east from Red Cross hospital, one mile from explosion.

Damage in Hiroshima.

Hiroshima. One mile south of the explosion.

From near at hand, Hiroshima appears as a toy city ruthlessly trampled on.

Nagasaki.   Industrial valley over which bomb was exploded.

Nagasaki. Reinforced concrete chimney one-fourth mile from explosion. This stack was approximately 100 feet high and 8 feet in diameter.

Nagasaki. Riveted steel stack toppled over by explosion one-half mile away. Note broken anchor bolts.

12.01 over Nagasaki.

INDEX

Abelson, Dr. Philip H., 36–7, 150, 151, 152, 153
Adams and Leverrier, predicters of the planet Neptune, 149
Adamson, Lieutenant Colonel Keith F., 86
Advisory Committee on Uranium, 86
AFL union, the, 131
Agnew, Harold, 212
Alamogordo Air Base, New Mexico, 3, 4; atomic bomb tested at, 180, 186–95, 202, 213, 270, 271
Albury, Lieutenant Charles D., 230
alchemy, 19, 20, 31, 36, 147, 253–4, 263
Allis-Chalmers Company, the, 140
Allison, Dr. Samuel K., 74, 192
alpha particles, 57, 58
Alvarez, Dr. Luis, 37, 212, 241; quoted, 207
American Institute of Electrical Engineers, the, 59
American Physical Society, the, 44
Anchor Ranch, 179
Anderson, Dr. H. L., 41, 54, 67, 74
Army and Navy authorities, 49, 86, 87, 165, 228; first financial support by, 88
Army Corps of Engineers, 3, 90, 198
Army Ordnance Corps, 86
Arne, member of Norwegian advance sabotage party, 97, 99
Ashworth, Commander Frederick L., 230, 240, 241
atomic bomb, the, 62, 90; explosions described, 4, 10–12, 194–5; predicted by Einstein, 85; destructiveness of, 86, 221–2; construction of production plants, 90–3, 116–20, 125–36, 137, 140–1, 155–64; announced by Truman, 114; secrets of, 123, 166–70; detonation of, 167, 169, 170; size of, 168–70; dropping of, 169, 217, 226; future use of, 173–5; tests at Los Alamos, 185–7; test at Alamogordo, 186–95; effects of, 195, 244–52; simulated, 197–8, 201; also see Hiroshima, Nagasaki
Atomic Bomb Development Center, 7
Atomic Bomb Project, the, 8, 36, 37, 44, 53, 68, 137, 153, 183, 197; government support of, 63–4, 65, 67, 86–93; officially launched, 91; $600,000,000 "expediting account" of, 92; also see Manhattan Engineer District
atomic energy, 3–5, 8, 9, 13–17, 19–25, 27–9, 34–5, 37–8, 42, 46–8, 55, 63–4, 67, 71–2, 75, 78, 84, 117–18, 160–2, 166, 169, 170–4, 183, 187, 223, 256–7; misconceptions about, 254–63; peacetime uses, 257–69
atomic explosions, 165; described, 4, 10–12, 194–5, 217–21, 236–8; study of, 169–70, 187–8, 190, 230; heat of, 171, 244; pressure of, 171, 244
atomic mass, 19–20, 40, 54, 172–3
atomic number, 18, 19–20
atomic power control, 29, 72–3, 77–8, 164
atomic power plants: described, 121–3, 125–36, 142–6, 158–64; also see piles
atoms: description of, 16–20; tagged, 266–7; also see fission, atomic
Attlee, Prime Minister Clement, 214, 231

B-29 Superfortresses, 10, 168, 170, 188, 196–243
Bacher, Professor R. F., 8, 189, 190

i

INDEX

Directorate of Tube Alloys, *see* Department of Scientific and Industrial Research

Distillation Products Company, the, 141

Doolittle, 201

Dow, David, 7

Downey, Chaplain William B., *quoted*, 209, 229

Duffus, R. L., *quoted*, 130

Dunning, Dr. John R., 35, 44, 51, 145, 258

du Pont de Nemours and Company, E. I., Inc., 68, 75, 78–9, 155

Easterly, Sergeant Elliott L., 209

Eddington, Sir Arthur, 17

Eighth U. S. Bomber Command, 110

Einar, member of Norwegian sabotage party, 96–112

Einstein, Dr. Albert, 15, 21–2, 25, 34, 39, 224; his advice to President Roosevelt, 83–5; *quoted*, 84–5, 87–8; atomic bomb predicted by, 85; *also see* theory of relativity

electrons, 9, 17, 18, 21, 24, 28, 40, 64, 151

element 92, *see* uranium

element 94, *see* plutonium

energy: atomic, *see* atomic energy; solar, 3, 13, 15, 17, 21, 24–5, 38, 170–1, 267–8; relation to mass, 14–16, 21–3

England, 50, 53, 64–5; government support in, of atomic research, 88–9; *also see* U. S.–British interchange

Enola Gay, the, 204, 206, 209–11, 214–15, 217–20, 226, 245

Falkenhorst, General von, 101; *quoted*, 108

Farmer, Dr., *see* Fermi, Enrico

Farrell, Brigadier General T. F., 8, 170, 187, 192, 202, 204, 205, 207, 210, 211, 213, 226, 242; *quoted*, 193–4, 205–6

Feld, Dr. B., 54

Ferebee, Major Thomas W., 217, 218, 220, 221, 226–7

Ferguson, Lieutenant Hugh C., 230

Fermi, Professor Enrico, 8, 31, 35, 36, 39, 41, 43, 44, 49, 50, 53–5, 60, 67, 74, 75, 76, 84–5, 87, 152, 165, 195; first to fire neutrons at uranium, 27–9; *quoted*, 59

fission, atomic, 23, 65, 70, 71, 74, 78, 83–7, 149–54, 159, 165, 170–4, 187, 193; of uranium, 31–4, 35–42, 45–8, 49, 50, 51–3, 54, 55–6, 57, 58, 59, 63; of plutonium, 63, 64, 153; military application of, 49, 50, 67, 83–93, 165; products of, 125, 150, 162–3, 170, 244–5, 263; in nature, 154

fissionable material, *see* plutonium *and* uranium

509th Composite Group (21st Bombing Command), 197, 200–3, 210, 213, 216, 225–6

Frisch, Dr. O. R., 33, 34, 35, 187

Fritt Folk, Quisling newspaper, 112

Fuaki, Mr., 247

Galtesund, the, 96

gamma rays, 31, 244

Gary, T. C., 75

General Electric Company, the, 46, 50, 140

General Policy Group, 90, 91

George Washington University, 7, 36

Germany, *see* Nazis

Godfrey, Lieutenant Leonard A., 231, 233, 235

gold, 19, 168; *also see* alchemy

Goudsmit, Professor S. A., 113–14; *quoted*, 114

Graham's law, 142–3, 144

Grand Coulee Dam, output compared with that of plutonium piles, 118

Grange, Red, 230

iii

INDEX

INDEX